WE DEDICATE THIS BOOK TO THE
CHILDREN OF TODAY AND TOMORROW,
AND THE RE-AWAKENING OF THE
CHILD WITHIN OURSELVES.

TRUST YOUR BREATH

Improve Your Breathing,
Improve Your Life

Commissioned by the

Trustees of The Great Big Trust

The Global Respiratory Educational Advancement Trust
Registered Charity No. SCO 37967

Compiled by

Anne Shearer and Heather Monteith

(Trustees)

A GREAT BIG BOOK

ISBN 978-0-9569977-1-5
A CIP catalogue record for this book
is available from the British Library.

Text layout and artwork production:
Bernard Chandler bernchandler@graffik.co.uk
Text set in Sabon with Cochin titling

Printed and bound in Great Britain by
CPI Antony Rowe, Chippenham and Eastbourne

Contents

Acknowledgements vii

Introduction ON BREATHING I

Part One THE SCIENCE AND ART OF BREATHING 15

Part Two BREATHING IS GLOBAL - BOOKLET 35

Part Three OXYGEN 51

Part Four THE NOSE 69

Part Five THE ABDOMEN AND THE SOLAR PLEXUS 89

Part Six ON REST 105

Part Seven RELATIONSHIPS 115

Part Eight THE POWER OF THOUGHT AND SPIRITUALITY 131

Part Nine ON VIBRATION, HUMAN ELECTRICITY,
           HEALING, LYMPHATIC SYSTEM AND THE HEART. 147

Part Ten THE ENVIRONMENT 169

Appendix 1 ON ANATOMY AND PHYSIOLOGY 183

Appendix 2 QUESTIONNAIRE 205

           BIBLIOGRAPHY 213

A NOTE ON COPYRIGHTED EXTRACTS

A selection of contributors from numerous publications and articles are included in the limited first edition of this book. A number of these were reviewed and underwent a critique. They were selected because their words seemed to match and mirror the positive life changes of so many people whose experience of Correct Breathing forms the basis of this book.

Any selected extract has been made from this review process and subsequent favourable critique because they are heartwarming, inspiring, admirable, accurate and spiritually true. The study of any of these books still in print and publication would greatly increase the reader's understanding of this enormously important and urgent subject, the global ignorance of which may well be at the root of societal degeneration.

If, despite our endeavours to contact the source of our quotations whenever appropriate, any inaccuracies or omissions in this book will be rectified in its second edition.

Reference details of all books are at the end of this book.

* * *

Acknowledgements

THE PUBLICATION OF THIS BOOK has been brought about through the continuing faith and support of the Trustees of the Great Big Trust, without whose vision its publication would not have been possible.

The text has been written and compiled by Anne Shearer and Heather Monteith, Trustees and founding members of the Great Big Trust in recognition of the truth of the statement "We have not inherited the earth from our fathers, but are borrowing it from our children."

The Trust is indebted to the thousands of people from all walks of life who have walked the 'walk of breath' and whose lives have been transformed. These include great souls from down the ages and wonderful writers of the present day whose experiences of correct breathing have inspired their writing on this subject whose time has come. "There is no army strong enough to withstand an idea whose time has come."

Grateful thanks to Bernard Chandler, our inspired editor and designer.

Acknowledgement and thanks to the child who is our teacher. We must respect and love our child within and the children in our midst who are our true teachers.

We also give grateful thanks to all those who have assisted in any way with the production of this book, through advice, practical help, administrative skills, encouragement and to those who provided the quiet creative space for its gestation.

Any inaccuracies or omissions in this book will be rectified in its second edition.

* * *

THE GREAT BIG TRUST was set up as an educational Trust to help people to re-gain the ability to breathe correctly, as a healthy baby breathes, who is the perfect instructor in breathing. For most people this involves re-learning how to breathe correctly and experiencing the multifold benefits on a mental, physical and spiritual level that come from it. *Trust Your Breath* is dedicated to all that is involved in the cycle of the Breath of Life; people who breathe in oxygen and have stewardship over the plant kingdom, and to the plants who take in our exhale of carbon dioxide and convert it to the oxygen we breathe. Without this two way cycle there would be no life as we know it.

Trust Your Breath represents a compilation of material on breathing, some of it is borrowed from what inspired writers through the ages have said and some of it generated especially for the book by the Trust. This first edition could be seen as a snapshot, or 'moment in time' in the work of the Trust and it is planned that there will be future editions which add to what is already here, reflecting the development of the Trust's work, which hopes to reach everyone, on a global level. It is only when a majority of the world breathes correctly that will we have universal peace, harmonious and responsible stewardship of nature, and the continuation of life will be assured for our children and future generations.

On Breathing

If only there were evil people somewhere insidiously
committing evil deeds, and it were necessary only to separate
them from the rest of us and destroy them. But the line dividing
good from evil cuts through the heart of every human being.
And who is willing to destroy a piece of his own heart?

Alexander Solzhenitsyn

THE GREAT BIG TRUST (The Global Respiratory Educational
Advancement Trust) was formed in the spring of 2001.
Its objectives are:-

a) To relieve persons suffering from incorrect respiration
   causing physical, emotional and mental stress, disorder
   or illness, particularly by the provision for such persons
   of therapeutic and counseling assistance, secure accom-
   modation, workshop and meeting places suitable to
   their needs.
b) The dissemination of information on the vital necessity
   of global respiratory correction by means of any lawful
   activity which could assist in the promotion of this aim;
   for the improvement of global, and individual physical,
   emotional, mental and spiritual health; the advancement
   of respiratory education; the relief of individuals suffering from stress as a result of incorrect breathing.
c) To advance education in the cause of limited or incorrect
   respiratory stress, disorder or illness, and in particular
   to promote research for the benefit of the public.

In carrying out the objectives we have been most grateful for the the help of the Lottery Awards for All Scotland, under its small grants scheme. This has enabled us to develop and carry out the initial training workshops, to create our pioneering accredited SCQF (Scottish Credit and Qualifications Framework) courses *Module 1, Introduction to Correct Breathing* and *Module 2, The Teaching of Correct Breathing*. The grant money also helped us with the collation and publication of this book. Our aim is to prioritise the introduction of correct breathing work particularly in schools, and an educational publication is in print. A copy is included in this book - Section 2. We believe its importance is obviously essential for all individuals in all walks of life.

Introduction

The Anthropologist Margaret Mead said "It only takes a small group of dedicated individuals to change the world, it always has and it always will."

In other words, "A man's aim should exceed his reach or what's a heaven for?"

We invite all those to whom this book makes sound sense, to contact us and join us in creating and setting up a new Children's Charter, so desperately needed for the world.

Our progress has been swift and slow, chaotic and highly organised, hilarious and very serious, the following quotations are from experts who understand the difficulties facing small and new charities:

> "Great oaks in the charity world often grow from tiny aberrant initiatives, which are so easily stifled at birth by administrative preconditions and conformism" said Phillips, who founded the law firm Bates, Wells and Braithwaite. "Some of the most brilliant charities I know in terms of the unaccountable impact they make on people's lives are some of the most untidy and unmanaged," he added.

"Vice versa, some of those which will pass every audit and monitoring exercise with ease, venture little and are short-lived in their impact."

We believe these comments could also be of use to newly formed aspiring charities with high ideals and great aims.

This book is meant to be read and absorbed as your intuition tells you. You don't have to plough through lengthy explanations of why's and wherefores, even although you may come back to them later. Just open any page intuitively and see if what it says feels right and seems to speak to you. Many people will say, perhaps sarcastically, "Oh yes, I breathe all the time." Don't try and persuade them, they are not yet ready, but you can be sure that they will not be breathing correctly, or they would understand the need for a book such as this. However we must never feel superior because we have personally discovered the miracles of correct breathing. Cynicism, even opposition, usually faces any innovative and new approaches, which is why we include the following paragraph by Machiavelli:

There is nothing more difficult to carry out, nor more doubtful of success, nor more dangerous to conduct than to initiate a new order of things. For the reformer has enemies in all who profit by the old order, and only lukewarm defenders in all those who profit by the new order.

Today's mighty oak is just yesterday's nut that held its ground.

David Icke

Henry James is quoted as saying "We need a moral alternative to war." Correct Breathing leads to Universal Spirituality which is the only moral alternative to war.

The creation of this book has been inspired by the experiences of many people over several decades whose personal lives have been transformed by correct breathing. Our work with thousands of people suffering from stress in all its forms, has led to an awareness that the way we breathe and use the energy of life can convert apparently irreversible human problems into self-healing and growth. Putting it simply, this is because the way *we decide to breathe* has an immediate effect on the electrical activity of the brain, in converting negative into positive energy and subsequent positive action, a process described throughout this book.

Each individual has an unlimited potential for personal growth and enrichment. The appalling level of human stress and misery is evident in all walks of life throughout the world today, from violence, addiction, abuse, mental and physical problems, poverty, poverty of thought, and stunted human creative potential. Obscene levels of wealth and greed are themselves forms of poverty consciousness, and in those who consider themselves 'rich' may be indications of the stifling of this potential.

The authorities who have been given or assumed responsibility to resolve the human issues of suffering seem powerless in the face of the escalation of social problems and greed. But within this dark night of the soul the light is dawning for many as they turn away from rampant materialism towards the work of healing themselves.

The dramatic way in which correct breathing can unlock the human mind, leading it to comprehend and deal with its own problems has been suppressed by a paternalistic approach of 'do gooding' rather than 'doing good'. We have ignored the wisdom of the advice that "the proper study of man is man". (Jung)

Several decades of successful experience working and teaching at this most fundamental level of human potential inspired The Great Big Trust's (Global Respiratory Educational Advancement Trust) decision to create a book by putting together the following pages. These contain testimonials, quotations, evidence, teaching material, from earlier and later philosophers, writers and thinkers, who have understood the utter certainty of the universal truth that we all have the power to solve our own problems through the wise alchemy of breath. Alas only a few doctors have embraced this truth.

In her book, *The New Way to Relax*, Karin Roon pointed out that a healthy baby is the perfect instructor in breathing and relaxation. A wise old lady called Enid Smithett, known only to few, declared that we are all equipped by nature to find our own way, and this for one moment will not brook the domination of another person. She also said "we don't have to live our lives through other people's megalomania, and we don't have to ask permission".

We would not wish to claim this publication is an intellectual masterpiece as dictated by the over-intellectualism of our times. It is submitted as a gift to the needs of our times, by a group of people, many of whom are over and approaching the proverbial three score years and ten. The pages contain priceless knowledge that has been distilled through the ages, flows tried and tested by personal and lived experience, and recorded in recent decades, which may have a positive impact at any stage of illness. Indeed, the book's message is eternal and joyful and will ring true for generations to come.

We believe that the disturbing increases in dementia and Alzheimer statistics, which also means that hundreds of thousands of people are involved 24/7 in caring for such human need, could be dramatically reversed by respiratory education or, in other words, the teaching and re-learning of correct breathing.

It is indeed tragic that a nation committed to intellectual attainment and a Curriculum of Excellence is apparently steadfastly ignorant of the fact that about 90% of our schoolchildren breathe incorrectly, therefore restricting oxygen to the brain. We wonder why so many leave school without even the rudiments of a basic education in English and simple mathematics.

> All is contained in the Divine Breath
> like the day in the morning's dawn.
>
> *Muhyiddin Ibn Arabi, Sufi mystic*

* * *

We have not inherited the Earth from our fathers... we are borrowing it from our children.

Native American indian

You will notice that the Trust only talks about **Correct or Incorrect Breathing**. It is felt that the words 'techniques' or 'deep breathing' do not give an adequate impression of what is involved, nor do they convey the sense that there is a highly precise intuitive instinct which requires a baby to breathe correctly *without prior instruction* because it is in touch with the *exact law of nature*. This law is embedded within the human brain, and it is one to which we must return in order to to use the energy of life correctly. This is not a technique. Whilst 'correct deep breathing' is meant to stimulate the instinct of respiration from its deepest source, too many people believe that 'deep breathing' requires a pulling in of the lower abdominal muscles and therefore *limitation* of breath, unfortunately a process taught to the military and in many performance sport activities.

Correct Breathing requires us to breathe down and up through the *nose* (not using the mouth), together with the expansion of the lungs from below the rib cage, with this expansion continuing into the middle and upper chest area. In this process the torso expansion resembles a capital D. When any container is filled, the process begins from the bottom to the top and is reversed when emptying from the top to bottom. In the same way the lungs fill and empty with air. Yogi Ramacharaka in his book *The Science of Breath* states:

MOUTH BREATHING IS THE MOST
DISGUSTING HABIT KNOWN TO MAN.

Improvement in the Correct Respiratory Pattern starts almost immediately, but the completion of breath correction may take a number of months, or even longer, depending upon the severity of muscular breath restriction. Steady improvement is always noticed at the physical, mental, emotional and spiritual levels.

Some of the material we have included in this book has been taken from the Great Big Trust's Level 7 course *Introduction to Correct Breathing*, as well as testimonials and assessments from Correct Breathing students, past and present.

Trustees' Testimonials

I was in a very bad place, not coping with life well. I was depressed and did not know what to do. I could not deal with situations. I was angry, I found the breathing by accident and started to learn how to breathe properly. I did not believe that by breathing properly I could heal myself and sort out my life.

It took me a while to believe in the breath work. I kept thinking that it would not work then I thought I have never believed in anything so why not believe in this. After that I did not question how or why, but began to notice the difference in my life. I coped better with situations and things became better and brighter. My friends and family noticed the difference, I became calmer and began to recognise what I wanted and didn't want, and was able to start to sort things out. My life began then and there.

I have now been breathing fully and connected for 27 years and I no longer feel angry or depressed, in fact I am happy and contented, in a good relationship and have a balanced life.

Margaret McKinney

Before I started my breath work journey, I was unsure who I was, and moved about in many directions for one experience to another.

At the time I found out about breath work I was in my early 20s and was faced with a decision on whether or not to have a major operation. I heard about someone who 'fixed your breath' – and I thought this would entail just a few visits and things would be physically better. Because of the severity of my health issue things took a little longer. Through breathing I found myself entering a healing phase of my journey and in doing so adopted a new way of life. Little did I know it turns into a lifetime journey and a way of life. This new way of life, through breathing, supports me daily on both physical and emotional levels.

Correct breathing has allowed me to take ownership of who I am as a person, and I feel privileged to have this awareness and practice in my life. I wish success to all those who step onto the transformative path of healing their breath. It is a journey well worth making.

Wilma

It is a wonderful thing to wake up in the midst of life and find the key which unlocks the doors of pain and stress which have imprisoned us as we journey through life, pointing the way to the fulfillment of our being. Consciously working with the breath, rediscovering our natural rhythm, is just such a key. Its powers to restore and heal our bodies and minds cannot be under estimated.

Bernadette

I was first introduced to Correct Breathing 19 years ago. I had a toddler and although I had many reasons to be happy with my life I had constantly struggled with anxiety and depression, social anxiety, fear and debilitating panic attacks. I used alcohol and drugs and prescription drugs to 'change' how I felt, but nothing worked. I felt unable to 'speak my truth', to just be myself and not feel I had to gain approval from my parents or try to fit in to what I thought people wanted me to be. I allowed myself to be walked over and gave other people more credit than I gave myself. I felt worthless. I was basically lost, though from the outside looking on you might not have guessed it.

Correct Breathing changed my life dramatically and subtly. I became able to make major decisions in my life, ones which also improved my own life quality and that of my children. I have learnt to overcome many of my fears, to be able to love myself and to have a voice. Correct breath is not a mystical treatment but is part of being human. I now realise that my ability to feel relaxed, to feel happy and full of fun but able to handle life on life's terms is determined by how much I want to 'tap' into this free power of the breath. I realise now that I am on a journey that contains many ups and downs of life, let's face it no one has immunity from these, but breathing correctly has allowed me to remain at my own centre, healthy, to be myself, and to have the knowledge that I am a unique person with unique attributes and contributions to make. In my relationships with my children and other people I am becoming more loving and accepting. I am now more able to enjoy life and the experiences it has to offer without the fear and anxiety. This is truly liberating.

Karen

I first came to Correct Breathing in 1995. My eldest son, who had been living life in a downward spiral had passed away suddenly two years previously, I was devastated and at my lowest ebb, no longer in control of my life and relying on prescription drugs to get me through the day. I had already tried various types of counselling and therapies, but none seemed to help me.

I found Correct Breathing through my love of butterflies. One day I came across a leaflet with a butterfly on it advertising the Metamorphic process and intuitively felt I had to find out more about this therapy. I went along to receive the treatment but was also referred to a therapist for Correct Breathing. Since then I have never looked back. It has opened me up spiritually and helped me face my fears. It gave me the courage to change my life for the better. I ended an unhealthy relationship I was in and found myself on my own for the first time in my life. Correct Breathing led me onto the path of self-fulfillment and self-discovery. During the journey I had to start out all over again with what seemed like nothing, but have since gone on to become a successful self-employed therapist who helps encourage and support others in their first steps on the journey of healing and self-discovery.

Now I look back at the past without regret. Thanks to Correct Breathing I view my life with a positive attitude and look forward to the future by staying in the present moment.

Fifteen years ago I set myself goals. I have achieved all but one which I aim to achieve next year. I find myself at one with the spirit and now reside in a natural environment in a place near and dear to my heart.

Mary Winters

As a child, I often had what could be called chronic sinus problems, lots of colds, soar throats, stuffed-up nose, breathing difficulties etc, etc. I had my tonsils and adenoids out plus my sinuses cleared. I later learned that sinus problems meant blocked tears, though I do remember crying a lot as a child because of the loss of my parents at an early age and the unhappy circumstances surrounding those events. I also suffered from undiagnosed childhood depression.

Gradually as I began to develop physically and spent more time outside, my sinus symptoms began to lessen, but because of my respiratory health history I was aware that my breathing could be improved. Life swept me along and I enthusiastically enjoyed all that it offered. My overall physical health improved and I had lots of energy. I did however continue to suffer bouts of depression and self-doubt which lingered on from childhood.

In my late thirties I moved location, leaving behind the city of my earlier years. This move was like turning the soil of my psyche from which sprang up new opportunities and involvements. It was at this point that I discovered 'breathing' and went through a series of breathing sessions. It is difficult to praise enough the value of those sessions and the experience of healing my breath. It was like a light being turned on. One of the most remarkable outcomes was that my depression shifted and I was able to gain a much clearer picture of who I was and what I could offer to life. As an artist and a creative person this was very important to me. I went on to become a practitioner and teacher of correct breathing and would recommend it to anyone who has an interest in themselves and life, it heals and enhances the overall experience of being alive.

Heather Monteith

Your breath is a funny thing. It sneaks around your body doing whatever it needs to do.

Surprisingly it influences your emotions, your thoughts and your wellbeing. As children we knew it, trusted it and played with it. However as we become older life's ups and downs impinge on our breath. We may feel at a loss and struggle to understand life. This is the time to re-engage with your breath.

However, do you want to, or are you already addicted to your weird behaviour ? Can you eloquently explain and justify it? Take a chance, and for your good and faithful friend, the breath. leave your emotional crutch in the bottle, packet or cellophane wrap.

Instead, breathe fully up your nose and take the air deep into your lungs. Forget the computer and boot up your diaphragm, Go for between four and 12 'correct' breaths per minute, in a relaxed position. Feel and experience the difference, have fun, it's free. The breath really is a funny thing.

Ewan Caskie

When I was diagnosed with a chronic illness (Rheumatoid Arthritis) in 2003, I had feelings of despair, confusion and great physical pain daily.

A short time later I was introduced to correct breath work. My life has gone from despair to being transformed in so many ways with new and interesting challenges to be addressed.

Correct breath work helped me a great deal to manage the psychical and emotional pain.

Correct breath work to me is like a fine tuning fork with wondrous melodies collectively pulling on a symphony of works, that spirals all three together, of MIND, BODY, SPIRIT; with a sense of knowing and a capacity of understanding that the focus and time given, be it ten minutes a day or more, for the honour of my own needs plus very good health has had STAR results.

My own general health and wellbeing has gone beyond my own expectations.

Recommended Recipe for Breathwork:

1 10 minutes (extra time optional) for today and always.
2 Toss in some practise with love and laughter for thyself.
3 Mix together with some patience.
4 Pass on with understanding and demonstration.
5 Benefits are general good health and well being.
6 Mysteries to unfold.

Price for ingredients - ABSOLUTLEY FREE.

Anne Freeburn, With Love

I first became involved with correct breathing in my early twenties when I experienced a lot of anxiety and fear leading to panic attacks and phobias. I found it hard to function with day to day life. Correct breathing helped me recover very quickly.

Through correct breathing I started to live my life in a different way, for example doing what's best for me rather than thinking too much about family and friend's views. It has helped me become more detached and less caught up in emotional dramas. Through correct breathing I have become more able to focus on what I enjoy in life, in particular spending time in nature and giving myself quiet time when I need it.

When I first started correct breathing, you could say I was an atheist, but ever since I am more aware and interested in the spiritual side of life. I think correct breathing has helped me be a more authentic person.

I listen to my relaxation tape almost every day which helps me to feel peaceful, let go of things which may be bothering me and have a lighter, more cheerful approach to life. During longer breathing sessions I feel very relaxed and energised afterwards.

Anne-Marie

I am experiencing many ongoing benefits in all areas of my life from correcting my breathing pattern, one being that I was able to stop smoking after years of trying many other ways to do so.

Lorraine

On reflection I think I lived the first forty years of my life like a car using only three gears when six were available to me, then wondering why I had various problems in my life, fear, unsatisfying relationships, obviously with myself first which reflected on others, none being as satisfying as I knew they could be. I knew I had the ability to do more with my life, but what ?

Then over a period of several years as I developed my work as a psychotherapist and trained hypnotherapist I began to discover that I was having to use words, intuition and knowledge that I had not at that time read in books, or been told about in my professional training. I found myself having to breathe and think from the lower part of my lungs and bring into reality an area now known as the 'second brain' which gave me information to be trusted. Feedback from my clients and their personal growth as a result of sharing the art of Correct Breathing, and the increase of wisdom within myself gave me the confidence to study the art of Correct Breathing from a number of sources with the realisation that the word for breath also means 'spirit'.

My life bagan to take off leading me to surge through fears which had formerly held me back, and a great increase in energy which allowed me to use the other three hitherto dormant 'gears' referred to above. I re-found joy and fun just being myself, a growing awareness of beauty in everything and a sense of being united with a great power for which there are really no words but which existed within myself and everyone, giving a wonderful sense of being in a loving relationship with a force which has never let me down and I know never will. We become re-united with the loving child within who knew all this anyway before our culture trained us in the 'religion' that intellect, materialism, profit and worldly success is all. It ain't! The power of nature, always loving is the boss. Life is full of love, pleasant surprises, fun and beauty. That is what Correct Breathing has tuaght me. I don't feel the need to pursuade you to try it but would love to share its blessing with you and the whole world.

Anne Shearer

13

Pressure has that tendency to steal up out of seeming nowhere when there is so much to get done in the day. But with so much to do it always seems easier to carry on rather than take that break. Much better however to recognise that stress has enfolded you and that it is time to ease back, and to do a bit of breathing.

It is like moving back into one's skin and feeling that yes I exist and that I am me, that there is space around me and thoughts, feelings and experiences of my own which give me shape, separateness, and inspiration, and which all restore my own sense of being. There is really no need to be a tethered player reacting one way or another to a never ending everbody else's world of demand. Time for music, time for painting, and for experiencing all the affirming aspects of life. People around me become human, and I too become human. Things of the world assume an easier perspective, and plans and intentions become achievable in a world of greater balance. Once again I find a sense of peace in my small-ness, the cosmos again becomes real, and contact is re-established with the creative mind of the universe. So much from the simple act of breathing.

There are times when I have forgotten when the unresolved pressure build up brings somatic response in my experiencing arrythmia, and more alarming vasa vagal related episodes. These events occurred regularly before I learned about breathing. They still occur but with decreasing frequency and are now only very occasional - indeed almost forgotten, and are of less severity. It is and has been my experience that arrythmia can be stilled almost within the instant by breathing, and that the vasa vagal episodes also recede instead of developing. With the latter it has even been the case that ambulances and their crews have been turned away, the pink form accepting responsibility duly signed, such is the confidence that returns when brought back into a sense of one's self through breathing.

Gavin Thomson

* * *

PART ONE

The Science and Art of Breathing

DURING THE COURSE you may hear information and facts about breathing repeated quite often. There is after all nothing we can discuss about anything in life in which breathing and oxygen does not play a part. In parts of the East breath is considered a food, an interesting thought. It has been said that air contains the finest homeopathic substances of all, which are needed for the renewal of trace elements in our body. These trace elements may be of very small amounts, and not scientifically measurable, but are essential to keep the engine of the body working smoothly. They resemble the tiniest cogs, which though minute, are still essential to a great machine; when they malfunction so does the whole machine.

Correct breathing ensures that we get an adequate supply of these elements which, as we have said, are too small to be scientifically observable, but we must remember that science does not yet, and may never, know everything! The other word for breath is spirit, which comes from the Greek language, so we must not ignore what the ancients knew!

The words 'spirit' or 'spiritual' are very important, because as you correct your breathing, you may find that a part of you, which has not been part of your education, is coming to the surface, and without being able to fully understand its importance, the word *spiritual* seems to be the only one appropriate.

By the time you read this lecture information you will already have received several practical sessions in correct breathing, which may have seemed to have the effect of stirring up parts of you,

you had not realised were there, even although you will have realised that this inner movement was important.

Remember that learning to breathe correctly again, because you knew how to do this when you were a very small baby, does not happen overnight. In his book *The Turning Point* Fritjof Capra, the physicist, forecast that "correct breathing is one of the most important aspects of relaxation and likely to play an important part in the future in stress-reduction techniques". Remember throughout this course that it is not about techniques but *correct* breathing, (the only alternative is *incorrect* breathing!)

We speak about what correct breathing really means; you also have this information in your Breathing Lecture booklet. This is what a little healthy baby already knows at birth, the only teacher being Nature, a process learned in the womb, and coming to maturity at birth. As Karen Roon says "a healthy new-born baby uses all the muscles of its trunk, abdomen, sides and back". If you know someone with a new baby, see if you can get a chance to see this in action.

HERE ARE SOME BREATHING DIRECTIONS: When you are going to practice breathing, (which leads to relaxation), first of all you have to give yourself permission to take the gift of time. Notice if it is hard to give yourself time, remember that time given to yourself always pays dividends for spending your energy wisely and noticing the good things that come to you. So try to stop being hard on yourself!

It is always better to lie down comfortably in a warm but not too warm room, with the window open, even just a little. Make sure you will not be disturbed. You can lie on your bed, but it is good if you have a little floor roll-up, full-length pad, or yoga mat. If you can manage without a pillow, fine, if not use as flat a one as possible. *You must be comfortable*, so have a blanket if necessary, and wear loose clothing. Give yourself a minute to 'touch base' with your body, and have a little stretch. Then think about what is happening in your body, and you will start to notice a

COMPULSION, that compulsion is a deep natural intuitive sense which is telling you to take in air if you are to stay alive! Think BREATHING. Think about any other natural activity you can do which will kill you if you stop doing it for a couple of minutes. Any tension in your body will have been instructed by your brain, that tension represents long-held fears. No, you are not being called a coward; most of this tension started to build up when you were a small child, the reasons not easily recalled.

VERY IMPORTANT TIP: We are meant to breathe in and out through the nose, that is why it was invented! You may read articles or hear people who should know better, tell you to breathe in through the nose, and out through the mouth. 70% of the waste material we excrete during the day is from the exhalation. The brain which only weighs around two kilos, sometimes less, requires about 35% of the oxygen we take in, and requires to release the polluted air from the brain. Only nose exhalation can do this. Try a little experiment for yourself. Do a couple of breaths in through the nose, and out through the mouth, and then another couple this time exhaling down the nose. You will probably sense that this is better for the brain.

Mouth breath exhalation implies negative thinking, and you are on the path to getting rid of negative thinking! Don't worry if it takes you a little while to restore full nose breathing.

Another reason for full nose breathing is that it helps to clear the sinus cavities close to the nose. When we mouth breathe, these cavities become blocked with mucous, unexpelled waste air pollutant. You may start to notice whether people breathe out through the nose or mouth, as part of your increased breath awareness habit.

Improved nasal breathing often seems to start to melt this blocked mucous, as it starts to drain away you may go through a period of needing to clear your nose more often, or expel phlegm orally, look upon this as a good sign.

When you start your first practice breath, try to breathe *out* first, which means down the nose as far as you can, which expels air from the base of the lungs. You will notice a strong need to breathe back up your nose, so without too much effort, try to breathe up as far as you can.

Remember the top of the lungs lie just below the collar bone. Give yourself time to think how difficult or easy that exercise seemed to be. Any difficulty will be because the muscles surrounding the lungs have become habitually tense or tight, and like any other physical exercise it takes time before those muscles become supple. These muscles are the most important in the body to relax, and when they become supple, there is a knock-on effect on all the other muscles from the top of the head to the tips of the fingers and toes, which will subsequently relax automatically.

A well-known psychologist, Wilhelm Reich, wrote the following words, In sudden fear we all catch our breath for the moment, some children have a life-time habit of catching their breath, and holding it. *"The sign of a well-reared child is its ability to breathe freely, it shows that it is not afraid of life."* Teaching ourselves to breathe correctly again also self-repairs any part of us which still retains childhood fears, as well as giving ourselves the best health tonic for life. Thank goodness air is still free!

As Professor Hilton Hotema said "If they could tax it (air) they would!"

ANOTHER TIP: If you have two fairly heavy books, even telephone directories will do, place one on your stomach just below the rib cage, and the other on your upper chest. You could use your hands instead of a book but will not get the heaviness of the book to expand against. When you breathe into the lower and larger part of your lungs, they will then expand, which will have the effect of lifting the book on your stomach, as your lungs take in a better supply of air. Continue your breath into the upper lungs, the book on your chest will rise with the expansion. Work up to 20 breaths at a time, at your own pace.

* * *

AND THAT'S IT. This is the basic correct breathing exercise. Because we all have our own individual breathing rhythm, and life history, the reasons why we have become poor breathers, are as many as there are grains in a kilo of salt, but the fact remains that repetitive correct breathing over whatever period of time is necessary will lead to great benefits in our lives. Our intelligence will tell us that as our muscles become less tense, the veins which carry blood all over the body, and are more or less parallel to the muscles will find it easier to allow the blood to flow round the body, unimpaired by tension from the muscles pressing upon them. It is the oxygen within the bloodstream which is required by every cell in the body, and every cell in your body is thirsty for that oxygen. Don't you think that it is worth spending a little time each day on repairing your breathing, in order that your cell-oxygen supply is also improved?

THERE ARE NO DRAWBACKS. If anyone on this course has had trouble with hyperventilation, which is really fear of breathing correctly or allowing oneself to feel good, the teacher will be able to assist you, and eventually hyperventilation can become a thing of the past. (There is a very good book, *The Hyperventilation Syndrome*, by Diana Bradley.) A large number of people suffer from the hyperventilation syndrome, which can be greatly helped by *correct breathing.*

Please note, our trained breathing teachers assist any course students in hyperventilation prevention. If you are liable to hyperventilation problems, just practice one correct breath at a time and increase by this amount as you become confident and symptoms disappear. If we are not breathing from the base of our lungs we may be prone to hyperventilation, which can be stopped at source if the inflation of the lungs comes from the lower belly. Placing a heavy book there will help encourage the lung expansion from that area.

When you first start practicing breathing correctly, you may find yourself feeling a little dizzy when you sit up after about

20 breaths. This is natural, and means your brain is beginning to absorb more oxygen. This minor symptom will disappear after a couple of sessions. You may also experience a little tingling in the hands and feet, again this is a sign that better circulation is flowing into the fingers and toes. You may be one of many people who find that their fingers and toes are always very cold in the winter months. It will be interesting to note if this improves after you have been involved with the breathing process for a few months.

There are two very important words to remember during and after this course. They are 'aware' and 'intuition'. You will become more aware of changes in your body, mind and emotions as you progress in this work. It is very worthwhile to keep a diary or reflective journal from the first course day. You may not write in it every day, maybe once every two or three days or when you remember. You will probably find that you become more aware of everyday events and their consequences, and you will also notice that it seems as if there was another little quiet voice inside your head, like an inner adviser. It is not a real voice of course, but again as you breathe better, that part of your personality which we call 'the true self' or true thinking self will suggest through your intuition, alternative ways of approaching events and happenings in your daily life.

Pay attention to this intuitive voice. If you ignore it you may take an action which will not give such good results as if you had listened to your intuition. Do not be upset if at first you forget to listen to your inner voice, it is a very refined skill, but one which will benefit your whole life. Almost the greatest benefit you will notice from this work will be an increase in confidence. So many people with great gifts, fail to reach their potential if they lack confidence. Our mature adult self never lacks confidence, so we sometimes have to encourage our 'non-confident' child part. As Susan Jeffers puts it "feel the fear and do it anyway".

As your breathing gets easier, you start to really enjoy using your true self, and other people will enjoy seeing this in you too. It helps them to overcome their own fears.

Starting to speak and act with greater confidence, may give you the feeling that you are being outrageous, all you are doing is releasing a stern parent part of yourself which has been thinking you are a failure, and criticizing yourself. Rubbish! Remember the words 'Be outrageous, those who achieve greatness are always outrageous!'

A WORD ABOUT BREATHING FREQUENCY

You will be given guidance in the practical part of the course as to how many breaths you should take when you practice. We start with five correct breaths only before we stop and compare notes. Then we work up to 10, 15, and 20. Taking 20 correct breaths is all that is eventually required each time you practice. You can of course do this several times a day. You may not be able to lie down each time; if you are in an armchair or other chair, sit up straight, place your hands on the lower part of your stomach, and on your upper chest, so that you feel the expansion.

If you are at work and other people are not far away you can breathe without the hands. You may find if you are in an office and say that you are going to take 5 correct breaths, other people may become interested and do the same, but don't do any more than tell them the basic natural expansion. A little correct breathing can improve tension in an office, and lessen computer strain.

Traffic lights can give you a chance for a few breaths, so as you approach lights which are green you can go through with relief; if they are red you can feel pleased too for you have a chance of a little breath practice. A win-win situation! Try to imagine all your experiences of life are bound up in a way that resembles all the skins of an onion. As we repair our breathing, and the brain is fed more adequately with oxygen, it seems as if the skins fall away, and between each layer are memories and events from all our life's experiences. Some may have been less than pleasant, and we have stored the fear they represented, the tension energy of which has become trapped in the layers. Exposed by the correct breath, they can be breathed away. The memories may be a little upsetting for a few days, but the events that caused them have passed. Breathing them out, has the effect of giving us more confidence. Like the saying "don't sweat the small stuff, it's all small stuff". Keep that as your yardstick, it can be very effective.

Karen Roon said that "teaching a small child to breathe correctly is like giving water to a dying daffodil". As adults we may still have a bit of the daffodil within us, give it the water of air!

The Second Brain

When you are lying down, instead of the suggested book, try placing your fingers over a point between the pelvic bone and the navel, just under the site of the umbilical cord area. As you inhale, try to expand from this point, and you will notice what appears to be a strong muscular reaction. It seems to be the source of the physical auto immune area, and its improved strength through breathing seems to reduce the frequency of colds. It is also the seat of the emotions, and referred to by Pierre Pallardy in his book *The Gut Instinct* as the Second Brain. Correct breathing reunites this area with the upper brain and helps to prevent hyperventilation.

To explore this a little further, correct breathing requires the full use of the diaphragm. The stomach, liver and reproductive organs lie beneath the diaphragm and also are massaged as we breathe.

The breathing movement massages these organs ensuring that they receive the oxygen and adequate nutrients they require to function in a healthy way. When a person uses upper chest breathing these organs lose this benefit and function is impaired.

The lymphatic duct travels alongside the spine at the back of the thoracic cage. Movement of this region is crucial for circulation within the lymphatic system - as this regulates our immune system it is a very important function. A good breathing pattern will move the fluid in a regular, rhythmical way. Irregular patterns may cause the fluid to stagnate, leading to health problems."

Tania Clifton-Smith, *Breathe to Succeed*

DON'T RUSH YOUR BREATH, ENJOY IT, IT IS MORE PRECIOUS THAN GOLD.

The other sense of this is that by breathing correctly, you can embrace the 'great big trust' that your life will develop and unfold in a positive way, just as it is meant to.

Testimonials from people who have benefited through using Correct Breathing

The Great Big Trust holds the original signed statements from which all the testimonials in this book are taken.

As you know, I have taught Science in Secondary Schools all my life - a difficult and demanding job at the best of times. In 36 years of teaching I have been acting Head of Department, Sixth Form College Tutor, and Team Leader responsible for a quarter of the pupils in one particular school. I strongly believe that I coped better because my breathing had been corrected by yourself. It is amazing that breathing malfunctions so easily and at such an early age.

I have found that most people breathe in 'panic mode' - shallow, tight breathing, which tips them over into anger and tension at the drop of a hat. Such people will not fulfil their potential, let alone keep calm in their daily interactions. However, once readjusted it results in clearer thinking, increased confidence, more thoughtfulness, better sleep patterns, a decrease in 'nerves' brought on by exams, relationships, and so on. People need space to find themselves and this is what correct breathing will do. The list of benefits is endless.

Mary

I've been meaning to write to you for ages but life has kept getting in the way. You helped me out last year before my finals (I've got long red hair) and I wanted you to know how much. I managed to get a 2.1 honour in law - something I never conceived possible - and your techniques continue to help me in all aspects of my life. I'm sad our sessions had to end.

However I feel the help you gave me and the things you taught me will stay with me throughout life. I'm finding it hard to articulate just how grateful I am. Thanks again.

Student, Glasgow University

I thought that you may be interested to hear how our 3rd year students evaluated their time at Edinburgh Napier prior to graduating last Thursday with their BSc Complementary Therapies (Aromoatherapy/Reflexology).

Every year we hold exit interviews with our students to help them identify key principles that they have learned, to reflect on how they have grown as individuals and to discuss where they hope their degrees will take them. Having studied a variety of subjects from anatomy and physiology to energetic perspectives on practice, this year there was a resounding response that the class you taught on breathing was the most important and valuable lesson that they had learned in the preceding three years. The general feeling was that having been taught to breathe correctly they could cope with the stresses of living, more adequately.

Lecturer, Napier University, Edinburgh

* * *

Limited shallow breathing has been proved to lead to insomnia, constipation, poor digestion, lack of confidence, depression, fatigue, high blood pressure, panic attacks, poor performance in exams and poor concentration, weakened immune system, floating anxiety, addictions, bad and abusive relationships, work place bullying, depression and suicidal tendencies, mood swings, ageing and allergies. We have proved that correcting the breathing pattern changes all of the above.

A good breathing pattern is between 10 - 14 breaths per minute, using the nose and expanding the lungs fully.

A Trustee of The Great Big Trust

Excerpts from Student Essays

GREAT BIG TRUST, LEVEL 7 INTRODUCTION TO CORRECT BREATHING COURSE

Often when a person begins to breathe correctly, they may have what seems to be a light cold. What is actually happening is that thick mucus-like material, built up through poor breathing inside the nose, nasal passage, sinuses and, for the smoker, inside the lungs, is beginning to release itself through the activity of the breath and the oxygen. The severity of the runny nose symptoms depends upon the severity of the mucus build up in the respiratory passages. The smoker may experience a hacking cough as tarry dark phlegm and mucus releases itself from the bronchia in the lungs and leaves via the mouth.

Margaret

Incorrect breathing causes muscle tension and fatigue which leads to neck and shoulder pain, low energy and poor sleep. Correct breathing reverses this and a person has the ability to avoid or fight the symptoms naturally, without medication. Back ache is also the scourge of western society as you probably hear people continually mentioning. Tension can be held in our muscles due to poor circulation and incorrect breathing. When we start to breathe correctly this can be reversed and although we may experience temporary small aches due to stretching the tissues and the release of toxins that may have built up over the years, this is nothing compared to the chronic pain experienced from back pain through poor breathing.

Isa

What other Visionary Writers have said about Breathing and Life

A doctor and researcher at a London teaching hospital stated:

Modern doctors are rarely taught to recognise disordered breathing, yet its chemical consequences can be far-reaching. They include:

- Disruption of the acid-alkaline balance in the blood as excessive oxygen is taken up and carbon dioxide is depleted.
- Loss of salts through the kidneys, as the body tries to compensate for excess alkalinity.
- Increased production of adrenaline, the stress hormone.
- Chemical changes in mast cells, which play a part in the body's defences against infection.
- 'Twitchiness' and narrowing of blood vessels. The heart may pound or flutter or miss a few beats.
- Nerve cells, at first over-stimulated, may later cause tingling and numbness.
- The brain gets up to 50% less oxygen than normal, leading to dizziness, faintness, feelings of unreality and an inability to think.
- Digestion is disrupted, causing stomach disorders.
  It is like an engine overheating, the governors come off all the systems, which then go haywire.

Someone recently showed me the Annual Prospectus of a large Spiritual organisation. When I looked through it, I was impressed by the wide choice of seminars and workshops, It reminded me of a smorgasbord, one of those Scandinavian buffets where you can take your pick from a huge variety of enticing dishes. This person asked me whether I would recommend one or two courses.

"I don't know," I said "they all look so interesting. But I do know this," I added "be aware of your breath as often as you are able, whenever you remember. Do that for one year, and it will be more powerfully transformative than attending all of these courses, and it's free."

Eckhart Tolle, A New Earth

So many of us feel that money is the most important thing in our lives, and that we could not live without it.

That is not true.

There is something far more important and precious to us, without which we could not exist.

What is that ?

It is our breath.

Our breath is the most precious substance in our lives, and yet we totally take it for granted as we exhale, that our next breath will be here. If we did not take another breath we would not last three minutes.

If the Power that created us has given us enough breath to last us as long as we live, can we not trust that everything else we also need will be supplied?

Louise Hay, You Can Heal Your Life

Breathing may be considered the most important of all of the functions of the body, for, indeed, all the other functions depend upon it. Man may exist some time without eating; a shorter time without drinking; but without breathing his existence may be measured by a few minutes.

Yogi Ramacharaka, The Hindu-Yogi Science of Breath

The percentage of civilised men who breathe correctly is quite small, and the result is shown in contracted chests and stooping shoulders, and the terrible increase in diseases of the respiratory organs. Eminent authorities have stated that one generation of correct breathers would regenerate the race, and disease would be so rare as to be looked upon as a curiosity. Whether looked at from the standpoint of the Oriental or Occidental, the connection between correct breathing and health is readily seen and explained.

Yogi Ramacharaka, The Hindu-Yogi Science of Breath

The combustion arising from the change in the waste products generates heat and equalizes the temperature of the body. Good breathers are apt not to 'take cold', and they generally have plenty of good warm blood which enables them to resist the changes in the outer temperature.

...In imperfect or shallow breathing, only a proportion of the lung cells are brought into play, and a great portion of the lung capacity is lost, the system suffering in proportion to the amount of under-oxygenation. The lower animals, in their native state, breathe naturally, and primitive man undoubtedly did the same. The abnormal manner of living adopted by civilized man – the shadow that follows upon civilisation – has robbed us of our natural habit of breathing, and the race has greatly suffered thereby. Man's only physical salvation is to 'get back to Nature'.

Yogi Ramacharaka, The Hindu-Yogi Science of Breath

There is a difference between a calm, conscious breath that gives lightness to the body and clarity to the mind and a short, mechanical one that cripples the body and dulls the mind.

Jenny Beeken, Don't Hold Your Breath

The plain fact of the matter is that most people do not breathe correctly. The majority of adults and, without exception, every adolescent I encounter in the course of my daily practice breathes to only about 50 per cent of their capacity.

Social pressures are to blame for this loss of natural breathing capacity. In early childhood, up to the age of two years or so, when consciousness of 'self' and the external world begins to manifest itself, children fill their lungs and abdomen with air – and empty both in a similar fashion. Later, when the pressures of the outside world come into play – introducing emotions such as stress, anxiety, timidity – the respiratory rhythm accelerates and the initial natural and spontaneous practice of deep breathing gives way to 'social' breathing, which is less deep and confined to the lungs and the bronchial tubes (and, even there, is only partial). As a result, the volume of air ingested into the body is reduced by approximately half.

Pierre Pallardy,
Gut Instinct - What your stomach is trying to tell you

The pause after exhaling is also important. The pause phase stills the mind. You may feel that you are doing nothing but air is actually still being exhaled. Most of us don't exhale for long enough; this is a common problem with people who suffer from asthma. The longer the pause, the more relaxing the breath and the more relaxed you will feel. When practising allow the pause to be as long as you want. Play with it – don't worry if you extend it for a long time as the breath in will come again.

Tania Clifton-Smith, Breathe To Succeed

Did you know that 70% of the excretory function of the body is done by breathing? The next biggest percentage is done by sweating. Urination and defecation accounts for less than inspiration and perspiration. Without breathing, the human organism would die of suffocation and toxic poisoning.

Leonard Orr, Breath Awareness

* * *

Learning to breathe properly and learning to use the power of our thoughts for our own benefit are the two most important activities a human can learn. Therefore, they deserve to be the focus of any educational system that is intended to be valuable or practical. Teaching Breath Awareness should be a most important theme in all schools.

Leonard Orr, Breath Awareness

As I look back over three-quarters of a century I realise that, after some false starts, I found the true vocation which escaped me in childhood (when I thought I was destined for the church), in adolescence (when I went to sea), and in the early manhood when I pursued a commercial career. I found it when I realised that my job in life was to pass on all I had learned about the technique of sound breathing.

In many ways I have received a deep satisfaction in the latter forty-five years of my life. I have 'cured' – to my own and my students' satisfaction, if not perhaps by the standards of those rigorous physicians to whom the very word 'cure' is suspect – several thousand sufferers from chronic bronchial diseases (including the dread emphysema) for which there is virtually no conventional treatment. I have alleviated the condition of tens of thousands more and I have helped as many again to build up their resistance to colds, 'flu and other diseases and generally to improve their health. I have also seen the importance of breathing recognised in many ways, and the only real disappointment which the years have brought me has been the continuing scepticism of many members of the medical profession – and perhaps the cowardice of other members who (as I know) secretly sympathise with me but are frightened to associate with one who is not a member of their union. For that profession itself remains almost as helpless to aid bronchial sufferers as it was when I was a child – and seems just as resistant to unconventional ideas.

William P. Knowles, New Life Through Breathing

"Although many people, medical and lay, have commented on my improved and sustained health, they are amazed to hear that the secret is simply that of breathing well. There is so much prejudice and ignorance about breathing exercises (most people think their natural way is sufficient) that few people realise how inadequately they use their lungs, and how much they could add to the joys of life if they would only take breathing seriously.

"There are two sets of people I would like to commend these exercises to. First, all healthy people, so that they *may avoid* chest and heart ailments. And, second, all those suffering from bronchitis, bronchiectasis, pulmonary tuberculosis and fibrositis, emphysema and coronary disease. These people will quickly start to feel better, have fewer complications, live longer and be able to work and play well, despite their disability." concluded Dr. A.B.

William P. Knowles, New Life Through Breathing

This brief account of the effects of a few pranayamic breathing techniques suggests that the traditional teachings of yogic masters can prove to be an interesting and rewarding field for scientific investigation. Such studies would not only increase our knowledge of basic physiological mechanisms, but would also point the way to new, simpler, and less costly methods for treatment of respiratory and other disorders.

Beverly H. Timmons and Ronald Ley [Editors],
Behavioural and Psychological Approaches to Breathing Disorders

Observing the breathing of a healthy baby or well-functioning adult, one will see the whole trunk expand on the in-breath and deflate on the out-breath. Healthy breathing follows a wavelike rhythm, is pleasurable, and is in good balance to the needs of the organism (Glaser, 1980).

Beverly H. Timmons and Ronald Ley [Editors],
Behavioural and Psychological Approaches to Breathing Disorders

* * *

We have to learn again that to contact one's depths is not to sink back into trancelike oblivion, but rather to submit to the difficult discipline of quiet attentiveness. This is a forgotten product of our culture that requires conscious effort. Culture means to tend to. Much as a gardener tends to the soil in order that his plants may grow in their own way and season, so attending to the depths of our own nature tills the soil in which, firmly rooted, we can develop into healthy individuals. The somatic approach of breathing therapy is aimed at providing the climate for this kind of growth.

Beverly H. Timmons and Ronald Ley [Editors]
Behavioural and Psychological Approaches to Breathing Disorders

Breath mastery must be practised on the physical, mental and spiritual levels to be complete.

On the level of the body, freeing my breathing mechanism is the ultimate medicine.

On the mental level, breath mastery is the ability to clear apparent conflict and to reach harmony.

On the spiritual level, breath mastery means living as the author of my existence, being in the driver's seat of my eternal vehicle.

Jim Morningstar, Breathing in Light and Love

Around 20 minutes of visualisation can be extremely beneficial. Not only will you have a feeling of well-being and enhanced energy, but the whole body will be toned up and the immune system will be stimulated.

Howard Kent, Breathe Better Feel Better

* * *

Affirmations

What is an affirmation? An affirmation is a positive statement of truth, designed to counteract a negative belief that you may possess. It is best spoken out and/or written in the present tense and created to re-affirm something that you want to become true.

I now have enough time, energy,
wisdom and money to accomplish all my desires

I am always in the right place,
at the right time, doing the right thing.

I now give and receive freely.

The universe loves and supports me.

With every breath I let go and relax.

It is safe for me to breathe.

I now breathe fully and freely.

Happy surprises come to me each day.

My ships come in over a calm sea,
under grace in perfect ways.

* * *

PART TWO

Breathing is Global

THE GREAT BIG TRUST holds the original signed statements from which all the testimonials in this book are taken.

We release here a copy of an educational pamphlet which can be used in schools, organisations, in fact by everyone. This pamphlet is released as our global gift in the hope and expectation that "great oaks from little acorns grow".

We believe that the time is now when the value of this work has come into its own. The poem below aptly expresses this awakening.

> The human heart can go the lengths of God...
> Dark and cold we may be, but this
> Is no winter now. The frozen misery
> Of centuries breaks, cracks, begins to move;
> The thunder is the thunder of the floes,
> The thaw, the flood, the upstart Spring.
> Thank God our time is now when wrong
> Comes up to face us everywhere,
> Never to leave us till we take
> The longest stride of soul men ever took.
> Affairs are now soul size.
> The enterprise is exploration into God.
> Where are you making for? It takes
> So many thousand years to wake...
> But will you wake, for pity's sake?
>
> *Christopher Fry, A Sleep of Prisoners*

THE GREAT BIG TRUST
Global Respiratory Educational Advancement Trust

BREATHING IS GLOBAL

www.thegreatbigtrust.org.uk

Learning without Stress
Simple Relaxation for life
Correct Breathing
Enjoy being You

A **GREAT BIG TRUST** Learning and Educational Publication.

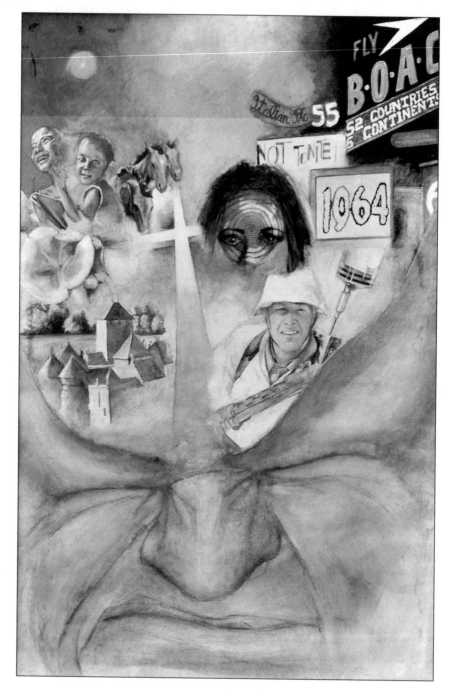

The picture opposite was painted by Janice Armstrong, former pupil at Hawick High School, the Borders.

This is what Janice wrote under her picture:

"This was my first attempt at expressing my beliefs. I wanted to place a cross between 'good' and 'bad' things, perhaps during a period when I myself was trying to work out what was 'good' and 'bad'. This picture gave me the confidence to continue with the theme of 'God' and 'Man'."

Can you understand what Janice was trying to say?

Discussion.

Intuition is a very powerful sense.

You can tap into your intuition and listen to what is right for you. Correct Breathing helps you to trust your intuition, which is very important.

Below is a diagram which shows what happens in each side of the brain. The Brain Rhythms can be measured electronically as frequencies (cycles per second) which are affected by the way we breathe:

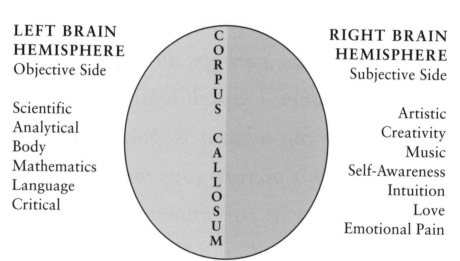

LEFT BRAIN HEMISPHERE
Objective Side

Scientific
Analytical
Body
Mathematics
Language
Critical

CORPUS CALLOSUM

RIGHT BRAIN HEMISPHERE
Subjective Side

Artistic
Creativity
Music
Self-Awareness
Intuition
Love
Emotional Pain

BRAIN RHYTHM FREQUENCIES or 'Gears' are:

BETA	Stress	15-25	cycles per second
ALPHA	Creativity	9-15	cycles per second
THETA	Meditation Trance	5-9	cycles per second
DELTA	Deep Sleep	0-5	cycles per second

When we breathe correctly the Alpha rhythm

dominates the brain and as a result we feel calm and peaceful. Some time ago, a nuclear physicist called **Robert Beck** went around the world researching the brain rhythms of people who can stay in Alpha rhythm and who can influence other people around them.

Do you know any people like this?

Robert Beck knew of the existence of **Schumann Waves** which are magnetic pulses which flow out from the earth and are always on the Alpha wavelength. When we breathe correctly and our brain waves change to Alpha, we feel peaceful and loving.

So do you think that the energy which created the earth must also be peaceful and loving?

Is that what we call nature?

Discuss this.

What do you think?

Here are some interesting facts about breathing:

We inhale approximately 11,000 litres of air a day (about $1^1/_2$ tanker loads of milk - a milk tanker carries 7,200 litres).

THE NOSE
How breathing can help stop us getting colds. Breath is for life, it is something you can practice. The nose - we are meant to breathe in and out through the nose. The nose warms and cleans the air you breathe in. The air warms up as it passes through the nostrils.

Correct breathing results in better blood circulation, renewal of our cells and a stronger immune system. What is the Immune System and where is it ?

Do you know about the waste material we excrete every day?

3% is in the form of solids

7% is in the form of liquids

20% is in the form of perspiration

70% is released in our OUT BREATH

Surprising isn't it?

If we breathe incorrectly this balance is upset.
Our blood-stream starts to become toxic because it is not circulating efficiently and getting rid of toxins.
We feel sluggish, tired and learning is difficult.
Correct breathing restores the balance.

We can train ourselves to breathe correctly, stay calm and positive and be in tune or harmony with nature and the energy of the earth. Isn't that a lovely thought ?

When breathing correctly you also discover that you have the power to reduce stress, fear, worry and exam nerves.

So how do we re-learn to breathe correctly?

Your first training sessions will take place at school under the guidance of someone who is trained in this work to help you feel confident with the process.
If you have asthma or some related condition you need more specialised help and would need a trained assistant or teacher to practice with you at school. It has been found that children will pick up their natural breathing pattern even it is only one correct breath at a time. Improvement and confidence in the process will follow quite quickly.

Notice we say *re-learn* to breathe.
We say re-learn because a little baby and small children usually breathe better than older people because they are more natural and closer to nature. Their breathing has not yet been upset by too much pressure.
In fact a wise lady called **Karin Roon** who wrote a book called *"The New Way to Relax"* said that a healthy baby is the perfect instructor in breathing and relaxation because the healthy baby uses its lungs and muscles correctly.

So...
give yourself 10 minutes. Find a quiet space or your bedroom. It is funny how difficult we may find it to take 10 minutes time for ourselves, but this is very important.

NOW.....

if you can do this, stretch out on the floor, put a little cushion or pillow under your head if you need it. If there is no carpet on the floor, see if you can find something soft to lie on. Make sure you are warm and comfortable. You can cover yourself with a blanket or duvet.

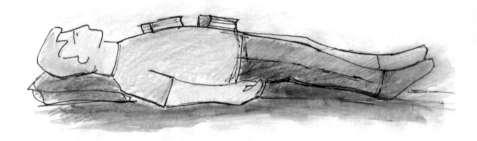

Find two heavyish books, place one on the lower half of your stomach and the other on your chest just like the illustration above. If you haven't got books just use your hands [see below]. This will help you to know that you are breathing from your stomach up to your chest.

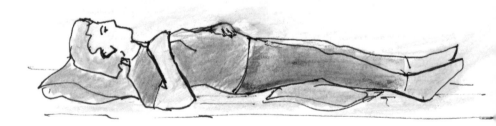

If you need to, blow your nose before you start. Make sure your mouth is closed as we are *only meant to use the nose* for breathing in and out.

Breathe *down* the nose as far as you can to empty out the old stale air.

Breathe *up* the nose as far as you can. Notice that your stomach and your chest will expand as your lungs fill up with air, proving that you are filling the lungs correctly.

Do this five times only, i.e. take five correct breaths to begin with.

You can do this twice a day at a time that suits you. It could be when you get up and before you go to bed at night.

Try this for about a week and if it feels right you can then increase the number of breaths to ten at a time.

In another week you can increase the number of breaths to 15, and eventually you will feel ready to raise the number to 20.

You can do this exercise whilst sitting in the bus, *but not whilst driving.*

After a few weeks you will probably find that you want to breathe correctly like this a lot of the time, and eventually it will become a habit as once again it comes naturally to you, sitting, standing, waiting for the bus.... Congratulations - go for it ! Correct breathing improves circulation, and the oxygen supply to the brain which requires at least 30% of the air we breathe. You will probably feel more cheerful, find exams less of a problem, and criticise yourself less - why not?

Nature made you and she did a great job!

This booklet has been produced by the Global Respiratory Educational Advancement Trust as an aid in helping develop and understand breathing as the basic law of health and nature.

The material in this booklet comes from The Great Big Trust SCQF Level 7 Course, 'An Introduction to Correct Breathing'. Our research shows that people who breathe correctly find learning easier, have fewer health problems, are more confident, can create satisfying relationships, get more fun out of life, have more energy, have good communication skills, find work they enjoy and which enriches their lives, improve sports performance... the list is endless.

Bullies don't breathe correctly. If they did their bullying behaviour would change, they would feel more peaceful.

If children who are being bullied learn to breathe correctly they become more confident and assertive, less afraid and less likely to be bullied.

Quotes

"There is no habit in life that pays bigger dividends, and pays them more promptly, than complete breathing. It is the source of your health, your cheerful spirits, your feeling of youth, your energy, and your relaxation."

Karin Roon

A Physicist called Fritjof Capra said:

"Correct Breathing is one of the most important aspects of relaxation and thus one of the most vital elements in all stress reduction techniques."

A famous yoga teacher said:

"One generation of correct breathers would regenerate the race, and disease would be so rare as to be looked upon as a curiosity."

"For breath is life, and if you breathe well you will live long on earth."

Sanskrit Proverb

47

Testimonials

"I would like to thank you for your help with my breathing, it helped me to gain a 2.1 law degree."

Law Student

Comments by children:

"I don't get so angry..."
"Concentrating on my breathing helps me calm my mind..."
"It helps me sleep..."
"I think it helps me listen more..."
"I notice how my breath helps me."

Napier University student's quote:

"The response from our students was that the class you taught on breathing was the most important and valuable lesson that they learned in the preceding three years."

The earth is your home, and
everything we have comes from nature.
Re-learn how to breathe correctly,
make friends with yourself and
nature, and care for the earth.
We cannot survive without
nature's harmony.

Quotes from:
Fritjof Capra's book:
"*The Turning Point - Science, Society and the Rising Culture*"

Karin Roon's book: "*The New Way to Relax*"
Yogi Ramacharaka's book: "*The Science of Breath*"

This booklet has been produced in partnership with Awards for All
and the National Lottery Fund

PART THREE

Oxygen

Oxygen is a transmitter of energy. It changes energy.
It acts as a catalyst and releases the energy within the cell itself.

Jan De Vries from his book Air, The Breath of Life.

WE PLACE GREAT IMPORTANCE on anything that we can physically see, how it is made up, how it breaks down, how it can be repaired, used with other ingredients. We can be referring to a building, an article, a person, an art-work, a natural evolution such as a flower or a tree which is visible to the eye. Since everything that is solid, still has its origin in some form of nature's creation, it will contain the element which we take for granted but is invisible. What is invisible we ignore, and yet oxygen or air which is all around us, yet cannot be seen, is the vital essential element from which all creation rises. For everything that we can see tangibly, there is a tool or a substance which we are confident will improve it or when used destructively will lead to its deterioration. **This basic tool of air or oxygen and its correct use must surely form the greater part of the as yet undiscovered force for the manifestation of harmony or health, as understood by humanity.** The fact that it is estimated that over 90% of the world's population are limiting their inborn knowledge of how to heal themselves by breathing correctly, must have a direct connection with the high levels of violence, addiction, cruelty, ill-health and destructiveness that plagues the nations of the earth.

The acknowledged mis-use of the *visible* elements such as earth fire and water, given to man for his survival, automatically ensures that the abuse of air or oxygen must be taken for granted. We quote elsewhere that the earth's unseen energy layer, all around the planet in the form of air, is on a vibrational frequency of alpha, a loving rhythm, therefore to exclude the use of this loving rhythm through incorrect breathing is tantamount to long-term self-suicide. For a visually dramatic reference, restricted breathing can be likened to the historic deforming binding of the feet of women in China and Japan. Similarly incorrect breathing can be likened to a self-imposed invisible deformity, where tension bound lungs enslave us to a life of conformity and ill-health.

> The magic with breathing is that it isn't just connected with the mechanics of the physical, ie. oxygen in... carbon dioxide out... purifying the blood and so forth - but is married to feelings. Feelings cannot be seen, breath or rather the invisibility of breath can be taken as a formless archetype. This essence of breath is known in eastern meditation as 'prana'. Howard Kent, the creator of the Yoga for Health Foundation, says prana is nearer to an electro magnetic energy, or closer to a solar energy. Our western upbringing which teaches us 'clever' concepts like the breath containing such things as oxygen ignores the feeling aspect of breathing.
>
> *Gunnel Minett, Exhale: An Overview of Breathwork*

Oxygen

LECTURE EXTRACT FROM
THE GREAT BIG TRUST'S LEVEL 7 COURSE
'INTRODUCTION TO CORRECT BREATHING'

Most people would attend a lecture if they were told that there was free wine on offer throughout the talk. Should we have to apologise if we mention that throughout this lecture free life energy will be continually available? Not only free but if taken into your body correctly would be able to save your life. All free wine would do is give you a hangover!

So, let us look at this miracle worker of which we probably

only use a sixth of what is on offer to us, that is if we are only using a small part of our potential, through incorrect breathing, because we don't yet know how to access the remaining five-sixths. This course is about helping you to access that remaining five sixths!

Did you know that 62% of the earth's crust is made up of oxygen? That is according to Nathaniel Altman who wrote a very interesting book, called *The Oxygen Prescription*. Much of the book talks about the benefits in health for people treated with man-made oxygen or ozone preparations, but there is an important section which talks about breathing as the natural way to absorb oxygen.

Oxygen of course is a clear, odourless gas which is dissolvable in water. You will remember the benefits obtainable from just being near the sea where the waves crash on the beach and the energy released contains an enormous amount of the health giving element ozone.

Facts and figures can sometimes astound us. We inhale approximately 11,000 litres] of air a day. This obviously requires us to expel the same quantity. We release the stale air, as CO_2, which contains the waste material from the cells collected by the blood, and eventually excreted in used, stale air. Perhaps it may help to remember that our exhale is a form of excretion, which is said to constitute 70% of our waste material. Few people know that only 3% of our waste consists of solids (faeces), 7% as liquid or urine, 20% as perspiration, and the remaining 70%, as we have said, in waste air. This is quite a good question to ask your friends, who will no doubt be surprised as they learn the percentage table of human excretory waste.

The point to make here is that only when we breathe correctly do these figures remain as a constant factor. Incorrect breathing will disrupt the natural elimination of waste, as the circulation of the blood, which acts like a vacuum to clean the cells, becomes disorganised.

If you are in a roomful of people where there is no proper ventilation, you will begin to feel tired and sluggish, as you are breathing in the waste products of other people's air excretion.

Sounds nasty, doesn't it? However this is happening in offices, classrooms and community premises countrywide, as we breathe in second, third and fourth-hand, the respiratory excretion of other people's waste air.

The air we breathe in acts as a combustion agent or catalyst in relation to the food we eat to create energy. Where poor breathing or inadequate use of oxygen is present, we will not be able to make right use of the food we consume. The process is named by Sheldon Saul Hendler as 'adenosise triphosphate' or ATP, if you ever come across it!

Oxygen or air is the basic currency of life. If you think of the other elements earth, fire and water, we have to pay for them. Often very dearly. As Hilton Hotema put it, "if they could charge for air they would".

Perhaps we should be wary of commercial products which offer oxygen boosts at fancy prices, implying that this is the only way we can get energy. Of course poor breathers may rave about such stimulants because they are just that, poor breathers, and have forgoten how to use 'free' oxygen.

It is like getting a commercial oxygen 'fix'. Poor breathers are really oxygen refusers, or oxygen anorexics. If they were to improve their breathing habits, the respiratory anorexia would no doubt disappear.

Incorrect breathing results in an inability to clear the body of toxins, which causes extreme fatigue, immune imbalance, cancer, heart disease, and premature ageing. From several decades of observation, a challenge exists to all those involved with physical or mental illness, to publicise the fact that there is always a respiratory limitation which is likely to be the *cause of the problem*, rather than a resulting symptom. Public debate could be instigated at the highest level to warn the public of this factor, in order to set up country and world-wide education in the adverse effects of incorrect breathing, or the cell oxygen debt factor.

Life function cannot be adequately maintained in an oxygen-starved environment, the environment being the lung food of the population.

A roomful of people, where the environment becomes high in CO_2 and low in fresh oxygen, creates a prime condition for the spread of infection, and in which viruses thrive. **Examples may be seen daily in under-ventilated and over-heated school classrooms and hospitals.**

In 1966 Nobel prize winner, Otto Warburg confirmed that the key condition for cancer is a lack of oxygen at cellular level. Where there is lack of oxygen at cellular level, food, however healthy, is unable to be properly processed, thus creating a cell fungal environment and food benefits become unavailable as energy. Many processed foods are badly lacking in energy creation. Efficient oxidation creates light, heat and electricity. Where it is lacking, metals rust and butter becomes rancid. Correct oxidation is the first line of defence against disease, because it breaks down toxic waste within human cells, which is then excreted as CO_2 in our out-breath. We refer to the % of waste material expelled as exhalation in an earlier paragraph.

Where there is injury, correct breathing speeds the healing process as damaged cells regenerate. Head trauma in particular depresses lung use, and correct lung use is probably the best curative process available. Gandhi, the Indian leader and mystic, deplored the demise of the spinning wheel in the home as industrialisation in factories took over cotton production. He said that India had 'thereby lost its left lung'. The left lung is directly linked to the right creative brain, and the creativity of hand spinning in every home kept the right creative brains of the people active. In taking away this activity, the creative brain of the masses began to stagnate. This idea may take some time to absorb, but reveals that Gandhi understood the link between the brain and the lungs. The left lung promotes oxygenation of the right creative brain, and the right lung has the same effect for the more materialistic left brain. He saw how the imbalance was being created within the population by the domination of materialism over creativity.

Parallel conclusions may be drawn in our increasingly global computer left-brain biased cultures, despite *economic* progress, some of which we could probably do without, as it has been made at the expense of the natural right-brain intuitive understanding of our need to prioritise correct use of oxygen, *the only life force.* In whatever economic success is made, there is no forward healthy economic progress if it occurs by incorrect use of oxygen, and therefore incorrect thinking.

In her wonderful little book *The Hyperventilation Syndrome,* Dinah Bradley, a New Zealand Physiotherapist, refers to the estimated 12% of the population who over-breathe, and quotes a schoolboy who (so wisely and intuitively) suggested that his mother was contributing to global warming by her poor breathing, and therefore increased CO_2 emissions. *A truly accurate observation.* From the clear mind of a child.

The subject of increased CO_2 emissions through incorrect breathing and therefore incorrect use of oxygen is one of the important points raised by The Great Big Trust, and urgently needs global understanding.

We have so much advice coming from all quarters on conservation, so many millions spent on global warming warnings, and yet the most obvious way in which everyone can contribute to global warming reduction is by breathing correctly This brings us back into direct harmony with Nature, as our brains relax into Alpha mode, the vibration of the Earth's magnetic field.

We might question whether it is individuals who have breathed incorrectly, and as a result thought and acted incorrectly down the years, who have brought about man's collective contribution to global warming.

Thoughts are energy and therefore important; perhaps we could collectively create the thought that individuals, families, groups, communities, small towns, big cities, and countries create a Correct Breathing Day, instead of going round picking up litter (they can do that another day) and meditate on whether a Breathing Correctly Day might be a more effective way to reduce global warming. It might create a regular habit. The better we breathe, the less oxygen we take from the atmosphere, (bad breathers take more than they should), and therefore the less polluting will be our out-breath. If the people who run the conservation projects haven't yet thought of this idea, by default it may suggest they need to learn correct breathing, or else they would have thought of the 'breathe right communities' themselves!

The wonderful book by Pierre Pallardy, called *The Gut Instinct*, reinforces our own belief that the stomach, particularly the lower stomach, is of such importance, for its correct use in breathing is similar to the base of a fountain from which the power of the water flows. In this case it is a fountain of air. This idea is very much part of Eastern traditional thinking. Pierre Pallardy calls it 'The Second Brain', and suggests that when our breathing only rises from the upper part of the lungs, then we are out of touch with our soul or true self. Eastern translation terms the gut or second brain area, which is activated through breathing from the lowest part of the lungs, as the sacred or sacral area. For us to ignore this area when we act, renders our actions soulless, untrue, false. In other words we are living a lie, if unintentionally.

Pallardy cites that there is a growing body of medical awareness which believes that this area of the stomach is at the core of immune-producing cells. Another writer has said that the muscles at the base of the abdomen are known as 'the girdle of strength'. Pallardy's references to the 'second brain' are reinforced by research in the USA. It is connected to the upper brain through the activity of oxygenated respiration. Professor Michael D. Gershon of NY Columbia University has published a book called *The Second Brain* and his findings are based upon 30 years of research into this area.

When we ignore breathing from the lower lung base, which stimulates the lower stomach or gut area, we seem to sever the link between the upper and lower brain, which means we act without intuition, spiritual awareness, and the great amplification of such knowledge which can only come when we are taking in the required supply of oxygen which is needed to inflate the lower part of the lungs. It is a well-known fact that if stretched out, the tissue of the lungs would expand to the size of a tennis court. Never let anyone else hurry your breathing, if you find that you are always hurrying, it will be a habit you picked up in childhood for whatever reason. **Now *you* are in charge, you are deciding to breathe with nature, who never hurries.**

The most common way to keep fit is usually suggested as taking very vigourous exercise. Of course regular exercise is good, but many people go to extremes, fatigue starves our muscles of oxygen. which can release harmful lactic acid into the bloodstream to make up for lack of oxygen. If you watch the histories of many well-known sportsmen and women over a period of years, many of them develop serious health problems, even alcoholism, which one might have thought could not have developed had they been breathing correctly. Such strenuous exercise is not necessarily spiritual, and only that which is spiritual has long-lasting benefits. Are we meant to emulate the days of Rome and Greece when physical prowess seemed to be worshipped as a God?

In his book *Breathe Better, Feel Better*, Howard Kent stresses the fact that when we breathe incorrectly or shallowly we use more oxygen, and that when we are in a meditative state our circulation can increase by 300%.

It may take some time before we appreciate the 'precious gift that is oxygen. That is because you cannot see it, it is odourless and tasteless, yet if we were suddenly deprived of it, and had a handful of precious gems, we would gladly exchange them for the life-force of oxygen. How we use it will define whether our life is joyful or sad, fulfilling or depressing. Whether at the end of our lives we go full of regret, or knowing that we have lived out the meaning of being true to ourselves. All depends on the way we breathe, and our subsequent life-creativity.

Gradually as you breathe better, you will find that you are no longer content to stay in oxygen depleted places, they are usually full of wrong breathers, or why would people stay in them. Do not be afraid to be the minority of one who says that you will have to go out to get some fresh air. You do not have to follow the herd. As you learn to breathe better, you will find that you develop a love-relationship with the unseen life-force which surrounds us, we are either for it or against it. Above all you will begin to understand, trust and cherish its power. Be proud of that knowledge.

Once again remember that small healthy babies are the best instructors in how to use oxygen correctly; their pace may seem fast but it is correct for them at their age, therefore their circulation is correct, they are perfect oxygen utilisers. No-one taught them, they just obey nature.

In talking about carbon-dioxide, the waste product of the breath, it is a necessary gas, because it takes away the waste material from the body. It is when it becomes out of balance through breathing wrongly that it creates a harmful environment within the human system. Just as we speak of the dangers of urine retention or constipation, so we can accept that many people can suffer from respiratory bulimia, anorexia or constipation, depends on whether they take in too much oxygen or too little. The results are still harmful.

There is a disease known as 'the silent killer', cancer. Perhaps we might think of oxygen as 'the Silent Healer'. We have free-will as to whether or how we receive it, it does not withdraw from us. If over many years we have withdrawn from using oxygen correctly, it will take time to restore the natural instinct we had as a small baby, but where can we find a better teacher? The side-effects of using oxygen correctly are confidence, joy at being alive, humour, generosity of spirit and, above all, love for ourselves first. The secret is correct oxygen use, the secret ingredient - love.

* * *

Testimonials from people who have benefited through using Correct Breathing

Breathing takes you into your natural rhythm. It relaxes the lungs, and makes the intercostal muscles work and become stronger, so our lungs take in more breath, and fill most parts of our bodies with it, so we can get rid of the rubbish (toxins) and be more relaxed, not just within the breath session but also outwith it. Also the more we do it, the more we remember to do it at little times throughout the day. It frees up parts of the body which have been frozen out of fear, or whatever gets rid of 'gunk' from the lungs. It gets the blood and gases balanced in the body, making us less nervous and panicky. When starting breath-work we might get tingly or sore bits, which means oxygen isn't used to getting into those places as they have been so tense.

It brings you more to your 'real self', and emotional and psychological stuff to be resolved, and sometimes you just process (integrate) it with your breathing. Breathing into a problem and pain in the body can dissolve it, and lift anxiety.

Breathing (correctly) balances the right and left brain, making a more balanced person, but on the occasions when things get too much and we lose the place, correct breathing makes our brains clearer, so that we can focus and think more effectively. It brings up old birth trauma to be resolved. I have been in a fog for a good number of months, but this breathing session I've had today has released this and also released a lot of fight aches in my body, I feel so much more grounded, relaxed and light than I've felt in ages. Thank you so much.

Janette

* * *

Assessment at Govan workshop: a) Really enjoyed the class. b) Thank you all, lovely day and a fresh start. c) Feel I reached and saw my inner child and happiness with parents. d) I am confident I will be breathing better now. e) Informative, relaxing, fabulous. f) Gained a greater understanding of me, and look forward to learning more in future - lovely day.

I feel that practicing the breath-work has released past pains and opened a new person within. I am more relaxed and focused.

Participant of breathing workshop

For seventy years I dreaded the onset of a 'cold', for it never failed to become a chest infection with all its attendant miseries and inconveniences.

However after listening to a talk given by the Great Big Trust on the subject of correct breathing, and after some guidance, I began to incorporate the breathing into my daily life.

Now after almost two and a half years, colds are an almost distant memory. I am also more relaxed and open to the joys of life.

I am sure that it would be beneficial to both old and young to have access to a correct breathing course.

Helen, a former teacher, in her 70s

It is recorded in the media that a young doctor who was able to perform more operations than any of her colleagues and still look fresh and relaxed at the end of the day, replied to questioning that her secret was in breathing correctly in order to have a constantly available energy supply. We understand that the medical profession, with the exception of dentists, have been recorded as having the highest stress level of all occupations.

The surgery would be grateful for any information on the wonderful work you offer.

Glasgow GP Practice

* * *

Excerpts from Student Essays

GREAT BIG TRUST, LEVEL 7 INTRODUCTION TO CORRECT BREATHING COURSE

Our complete health depends on many things, but one of the most important factors is how we breathe. From the moment we are born, when we take our very first breath, until the moment at the end of our life when we take our last breath, breathing is something the body knows how to do for basic survival. At birth our whole bodies breathed. With every cell we absorbed oxygen, breathing life into our system, every bone in our body, and all our muscles and organs moved with every breath, every nerve was stimulated by it, every blood cell transported it and every second was measured by the inhalation and exhalation of the breath. Today most of us have failed to remember what it feels like to breathe fully with the rhythm of the new born infant. We may have forgotten this but we have not lost it. Breathing is an automatic process, but when you unconsciously hold or restrict your breath through habit, breathing becomes restricted and distorted. This distortion of breath allows you to survive, but not to flourish, so to restore what has always been part of you involves conscious awareness and participation. Breathing correctly is not a matter of adding anything but is instead a way of re-discovering the spontaneity of our breath and has to do with taking away the obstructions that we have created both consciously and unconsciously. In restoring the broadness of our breathing we also restore many other capacities in our lives.

Margaret

In conclusion we can say that chronic pain, mental suffering and disease are caused by a lack of oxygen in our bodies. The only way this life giving substance can get into our bodies is through our breath. It is therefore critically important that we are all made aware of this simple truth and start to recognise our breathing as one of the most important things in our life. We will then be able to liberate ourselves from the learned destructive behaviour of anger, fear, worry and jealousy. Only then will we be able to experience and express unconditional love which is the greatest healing force on the earth. Consequently we will rescue the earth from devouring itself through human created diseases such as hate and war. We may then create a better society, one bursting with positive relationships and loving communication.

Ewan

Restricted breathing is often caused by unresolved fear. This fear can generally be related back to childhood. The fear causes throat muscles to be restricted, leading to hyperventilation or over-breathing. When we breathe incorrectly, and a situation arises where we feel threatened, we start to become anxious; our breathing speeds up; we take in more oxygen - but we are less able to expel carbon dioxide from our lungs; we may feel light-headed or in the worst case scenario lose consciousness altogether. Correct breathing provides an antidote to the body's reactions to deep seated fear. Incorrect breathing is associated with anxiety and stress. Breathing directly from the diaphragm induces calm.

Mary

What other Visionary Writers have said about Breathing and Life

We are indeed reminded of the mystical and practical importance which the ancient world gave to breathing whenever we use not only such words but others like 'pneumatic' and even 'soul'. The Latin, Greek or Eastern roots of them all combine the ideas of mental and spiritual well-being with that of a movement of air.

Breath, too, was at the heart of the philosophy of the Greek school of physicians called the *therapeuti,* perhaps the founders of all preventive medicine. But otherwise this tradition – so old, so firmly-rooted and so widespread that it alone should convince any unprejudiced person that deep breathing as an aid to health is worth taking very seriously – seems to have passed underground, at least in the western world, for over fifteen hundred years.

William P. Knowles, New Life Through Breathing

I have already expressed my belief that most of us suffer from scraping along on a minimum consumption of air. We keep alive, of course, just as a prisoner of war or a pauper can keep alive for years on far less food than he or she really needs. But insidi-ous oxygen starvation, like the malnutrition of too few calories and vitamins, leads to mental depression, physical sluggishness, at least minor illnesses, and at length to a shortened life-span.

Air is neither rationed nor expensive, and all that really prevents us taking as much of it as we need is laziness. But we may also have to overcome a prejudice that we should not *need* training to be able to breathe properly.

William P. Knowles, New Life Through Breathing

The only thing that gives humans, animals, plants, *life* is air-oxygen. We may not accept this statement at this point of our comprehension, but when we reject life we can only reject the only force of life we have been given, which is air. We only accept life when, as at birth, we breathe, but *very few people breathe correctly – about ten per cent.*

So you might say most people are choosing to deny life and so die, because as soon as we experience the opposite force to life, which is fear, we limit our breathing.

We don't need to bother about the atom bomb, we're extin-guishing ourselves quite well without it, it's cheaper too.

Anne Gillard Shearer, LOVE, DRUGS… or any city like Glasgow

* * *

Donald M. Epstein, D.C., author of *The Twelve Stages of Healing* and *Healing Myths, Healing Magic*, has often said that healing is "an inside job". He means that the most essential components to healing, such as life force, harmony, regeneration, and repair are not given to us by others but come from within. Innate healing power is part of our birthright and is within reach of every one of us.

Nathaniel Altman, The Oxygen Prescription

Roughly speaking, inhalation takes something over a second, and exhalation the same. In other words, we inhale and exhale some 20 times a minute, or 1,200 times every hour, and around 15,000 times a day, with allowance made for slower breathing patterns during non-waking hours. I once calculated that on an annual basis, the typical human inhales and exhales roughly 5.5 million times. Breathing imparts a natural rhythm to our lives and is a precondition of survival. By re-oxygenating the blood, we keep our vital organs functioning, not least the two most vital organs of all, the abdomen and the upper brain.

The daily pressures of modern life impact negatively on our breathing patterns. Sedentary lifestyles and junk food exacerbate the problem. On the whole, we breathe more rapidly and less fully today than we did 20 or 30 years ago.

Pierre Pallardy,
Gut Instinct - What your stomach is trying to tell you

Once you have mastered the technique of inflating and emptying your abdomen at the same time as your lungs, you will impart new life and vibrancy to your abdomen and help it fulfil its role as your second brain. The link between this second brain and the upper brain – and I cannot emphasise this too much – is an essential component of a healthy lifestyle and an invaluable tool in warding off all manner of complaints and disorders. Where this two-brain harmony is not in place, the abdomen cannot function as it should. By the same token, a healthy abdomen is a precondition of the optimal functioning of the upper brain, which is the seat of our senses, intelligence, intuition and emotions.

Pierre Pallardy,
Gut Instinct - What your stomach is trying to tell you

Breathing has three main functions:

When we breathe in we **take in oxygen,** which travels through the nasal passages to the lungs to enter the bloodstream. Oxygen is necessary for the body to convert food into energy in order to 'power' the body and enable all cells to function.

When we exhale we **breathe out carbon dioxide,** the end result of this metabolism.

Breathing **preserves the acid-alkaline balance** (pH). This is the balance between the amount of carbonic acid and bicarbonate in the blood; this must be kept at a constant value of 7.4.

Tania Clifton-Smith, Breathe To Succeed

The present writer's experience. In 1979, 1739 patients confirmed by respiratory physiological analysis amply supports this view (concerning the efficiency of correct breathing exercises) More than 1,000 patients have received a course of breathing retraining and relaxation in the physiotherapy department. Symptoms are usually abolished within one to six months. Some young patients require only a few weeks, while older or more severe cases may take many months, 75% are completely free of all symptoms at 12 months. 20% are left with occasional mild symptoms only, and these do not trouble them. They lose their anxiety. Only about one in twenty are quite intractable.

Dr. Claude Lum, Addenbrooke's and Papworth hospitals, Cambridge

The volume of air we breathe in every day is approximately five times larger than the volume of food and drink we consume. On average a normal, healthy person breathes 12 – 14 times per minute.

Gunnel Minett, Exhale: An Overview of Breathwork

When we breathe naturally the body receives all the oxygen it needs to function optimally. Our natural breathing also relaxes the body so that circulation functions well and supplies the various parts of our body with sufficient energy.

Gunnel Minett, Exhale: An Overview of Breathwork

The brain too, though doing no apparent physical work, is a great consumer of oxygen – and an even greater hater of the carbon dioxide which accumulates in the bloodstream and fatigues us mentally and physically when our 'gas-exchange' is not working properly.

William P. Knowles, New Life Through Breathing

This is the most positive thing I have learned in teaching adults to breathe. It is that the breathing mechanism is repairable. Even birth trauma can be repaired.

I have taught infants only a few days after birth how to breathe and I have taught people over ninety years after birth how to breathe. Breathing properly is a perpetual source of miracles.

Leonard Orr, Breath Awareness

Breathing is a fast, harmless, and safe way of making your mind and emotions safe and harmless. It has already proven itself to be an effective solution to the teenage drug problem. Simple breathing enables teachers and students to stay relaxed and to enjoy the learning process. It enables people to release disturbed emotions and thoughts that block concentration and the learning process.

Leonard Orr, Breath Awareness

Breath is energy. It is one of the greatest medicines known to man. One big drawback of ill health is the lack of energy, and fear of it getting worse. A sick person can be so lacking in energy that the slightest thing upsets them. A drink of water or a meal not produced promptly can be a real bore. As well as physical weakness there is a moral weakness. Insecurity becomes paramount. Hence inner strength is needed. With the breath one not only boosts energy, but one's immune system is greatly aided.

Eric Taylor, Breath Therapy

The sinus system acts like a ventilation system in the head. One of its duties is to restore oxygen to the head and dispose of it via the frontal sinuses into the nostrils.

Jan de Vries, AIR, The Breath of Life

Inspirational quotes to help on your Breathing Journey

A man's value to the community primarily depends on how far his feelings, thoughts, and actions are directed towards promoting the good of his fellows.

Albert Einstein

A merry heart doeth good like a medicine; but a broken spirit drieth the bones.

The Bible

Scatter Joy.

Ralph Waldo Emerson

PART FOUR

The Nose

IN CORRECTING OUR BREATHING, and possibly beginning to read books about correct breathing, of which there are too few, we may notice references to nose breathing versus mouth breathing. The most vivid of these can be read in Ramacharaka's classic work on breathing, *The Science of Breath*, which says "Many contagious diseases are contracted by the **disgusting** habit of mouth breathing, and many cases of cold and catarrhal afflictions are also attributable to the same cause."

Jonathan Daemion in his book *The Healing Power of Breath* states, "the nose is beautifully designed to inhale air, a) because the hairs inside the nostrils trap dust and dirt and b) because the air is warmed as it travels up the nose before entering the tender lung tissue." Breathing through the mouth dries up the airways. With growing self-awareness we begin to notice where and in what circumstances we ourselves may be breathing through the mouth (incorrectly) and find that this is often associated with negative thinking.

A very small baby always breathes through the nose, indeed there has been a suggestion that the cot death syndrom may be due to the fact that a small baby vomits or has breathing problems while deeply asleep because it is 'programmed' by nature to breathe through the nose. This makes it virtually impossible for it to choose to breathe through the mouth as an alternative. Accordingly this may cut off its air supply and can lead to choking and death. When vomit blocks the nasal passage at the back of the throat the new baby does not have an alternative instinct at this stage to breathe through the mouth. We believe this is a suggestion well worth considering. A child seems to recognise that in breathing through the nose it is breathing with its spirit. When frightened a child will hold its breath believing that in so doing it cannot be seen. In a situation where a child is reared in a stressful environment, in which it is constantly afraid or anxious, it will eventually cease to breathe through the nose and change to mouth breathing as a form of survival. Eventually this becomes a permanent state, the sinuses, which are apertures around the nose and the forehead, are no longer cleared by the energy of regular air passage, and become clogged with the debris of respiratory mucus. We have seen many children and adults with sinus problems which one writer has named as *blocked tears*. i.e. "where no tears fall from the eyes, other organs weep".

Mouth breathing leads to inadequate stimulation of the neural olfactory pathway to the brain.

The nose performs the important functions of moistening and warming the incoming air and of filtering out impurities before it enters the nasal passage and the lungs. The importance of the nose is universally underestimated, it produces a gas called nitric oxide which is important as it sterilises the incoming air, it continually maintains clearance of mucus, preventing mucus from gathering, thickening, and becoming infected. Nitric Oxide also facilitates the uptake of oxygen through the pulmonary blood flow.

Tania Clifton-Smith says in her book *Breathe to Succeed* "as a therapist I am so convinced of the importance of nose breathing that every time I see people who are mouth breathers I am tempted to approach them and beg them to start using their nose to breathe".

The Nose

This chapter is taken from the book *"The Earth Can Heal Itself, Can You?"* by Anne Shearer, with her permission.

A few years ago I would never have believed that I could feel so passionately about what I suppose would be called 'the right use of the nose'. Until fairly recently as far as I was aware, the nose was just an appendage on the front of the face, occasionally to be cleared. When I was a child I used a handkerchief to blow my nose, probably embroidered with a flower motif in one corner. I still have a few of these within, what was called in my childhood, a *handkerchief-sachet,* one of my first achievements in my primary school sewing class. It was worn acoss one shoulder, and hung to the side. A good place to hide the odd sweet. My father used to use a dozen or more large white cotton handkerchiefs each week, which my mother boiled on washing day. As a nine-year old amateur I had the job of pulling out the corners and creases, and ironing into exact immaculate white squares for his working days in his office. Nowadays most people use a tissue.

The proper use, science and function of the nose is one of the most vital health lessons we could learn, and I believe *need to learn.* In the past few weeks, having once again been confronted by the abbreviations IQ, I realised they invariably apply to *intellectual* intelligence, whereas increasingly I am concerned that universally we seem to neglect another more important EQ measurement. That of *emotional intelligence* which, I am positive, must precede intellectual intelligence, or the latter is a hollow column of meaningless figures. Nose science develops the use of emotional intelligence.

At eighty, it is only in the last twenty years I have realised that in breathing correctly, we are meant to breathe in through the nose, *and out through the nose.* This matters so much to me nowadays, that I watch with horror the actors on TV who seem to spend their time breathing out through the mouth in any exclamation of negativity, while my emotional EQ is registering the amount of additional polluting CO_2 they are discharging into the atmosphere by exhaling in this way. To me these days exhaling through the mouth seems as ridiculous as putting food up the nose in order to eat!

I do understand that we *can* use the mouth to get air in and out of the lungs, but believe that should be only in an extremity, just as only in an extremity we see someone being fed through tubes in the nose in a hospital.

Someone who is hyperventilating breathes in and out through the mouth, because they are locked in a state of fear and panic. When we *over-exercise*, we bring mouth breathing into use. *I am not sure if we are meant to over-exercise!* You can easily recall a memory of an athlete who is constantly over-exercising in competitive sports bending over in respiratory extremis and using the mouth for breath recovery. I do not have a great deal of sympathy for competitive exercise to try and prove oneself superior to someone else. I believe it is morally questionable to want to prove myself better than another, in any form of man-made test.

I note how many competitive athletes seem to develop later life-threatening health problems, and that the so-called competitive life-style does not necessarily ensure a longer life span or freedom from later life ill-health or disease.

Cricketers may be the exception! I am sure that many will disagree with me on my comments in these last lines, but I speak from observation.

There are many beautiful ways to exercise the body which do not impose competition, or the unnatural strain of oral exhalation.

Nature never seems to run like mad, except possibly when she is reacting to man-made excesses. She then has no option but to bring herself back into balance in apparently violent ways such as natural disasters.

The astonishing discoveries which I have made concerning the nose have come to me *despite* rather then *because* of my therapeutic training.

In my training as a psychotherapist, or any subsequent training I have undergone, any mention of the nose has been noticeably absent. My discoveries and training have come from working with many people in breath repair, the unintentional re-emergence of my own emotional IQ, and gems of information which mirrored my own findings, from too few writers who understand the language of the nose.

This true science of the nose seems to be rarely understood, because medical science and treatment appears to be involved with intellectual IQ, and not its connection with the emotions. Again the concern with symptoms rather than cause.

If a highly-paid medical professional concerned with the nose does not breathe correctly themselves, as some do not, I cannot see how they know how to prevent the symptoms of the patient from re-occurring.

I remember someone well-known to me who was treated as a young person for what are called nasal polyps (a growth protruding from the mucus lining of the nose). From what I recall of the emotional environment of that highly intelligent young person's childhood, his relationship with his father had been disastrous. I now believe that the growth of his nasal polyps was the result of breath-holding from fear of his father during his childhood. In holding his breath from apprehension, the suppression of the circulation of nasal oxygen would, I suppose, have created the build-up of surplus energy tissue.

Despite the operation to remove the physical problem, as a man, he spent his whole life affected by the emotional trauma from his childhood, and his eventual death mostly from alcohol and nicotine abuse despite a highly successful intellectual career, reflected I believe the *nasal* tragedy of his emotional life.

It seems appalling to reflect that in the boxing world, the main aim is to render your opponent helpless by one of several lethal blows, and the one to the nose is most vital. What an occupation, to encourage the one organ of the body which was invented by nature to convey the life-force to the lungs to be so abused. Obviously such an injury will quickly limit air to the lungs, and therefore loss of energy. Use of the mouth as an emergency supply is restricted by the gum-shield. How obscene is this parody for gruesome entertainment, almost a hand-me-down from the time of the Roman gladiators! While the audience screams and gloats.

Only a few writers have spoken as graphically as I would wish, on the right use and function of the nose. One or two span several generations, from Yoga Ramacharaka, who spoke of "mouth breathing as being the most disgusting form of breathing known to man", and Tania Clifton-Webb who runs a breathing practice in New Zealand who, in her recent book *Breathe for Success,* speaks of nose-breathing as "Nature's Second-best Kept Secret". *Secret,* because I believe that intentionally or unintentionally our intellectually motivated medical hierarchal IQ treatment of its responsibility to the masses has withheld from those masses the secrets of health which, if understood, would deprive the medical and pharmaceutical world of much of their livelihood. For those masses would then recover the true secrets of health known from within. The secrets of healthy living are thrown at us ad nauseum, in various forms of media coverage, but what is withheld is the single most important health information that of *correct* breathing.

Unfortunately many health educationalists are not healthy breathers themselves, particularly concerning the emotional IQ implications of correct nasal respiratory function. Nature's No. 1 Law of Health.

I have lost count of some yoga books, health books and health teachers who will tell you that you must breathe in through the nose, and out through the mouth. I disagree with this, which I believe to be erroneous, and against the laws of Nature.

Now try this little exercise. Find a quiet room, and stand upright comfortably. Think of slowing down all your reactions, then try this breath experiment without haste and with awareness. Listen to what is happening in your body, especially the lungs as you: (a) Breath in through the nose, and out through the mouth. Then: (b) Breathe in through the nose, and out through the nose. Do notice that when you breathe as in b, do you discover that there is an impulse to draw the next breath in from a lower part of your lungs?

Repeat this little exercise several times, until you understand that there is a subtle difference between (a) and (b).

I have come to call (a) *carnal breathing,* and (b) *spiritual breathing.* When you really study this subject, you are apt to come up with new verbal inventions to describe the art of respiration. This often happens when I attempt to describe aspects of breath use.

They don't teach soldiers correct breathing from what I can gather. The (b) method, would make it much harder to go out and kill your enemy, you might even refuse to do so, your conscience would not let you. To be a fighter you have to have a lot of held tension, in order to discharge it in aggressive action. The (a) breathing method encourages us to suppress loving emotion which complicates the issue when you have to summon tension to kill. To breathe correctly makes it impossible to kill. On the other hand when man is eventually civilised enough to discover other ways to disarm his opponent by the power of breath and thought, he will be able to utilise higher spiritual means to deflect aggression.

Understanding the fine and full subtlety of nose breathing does not happen overnight, you have to think about months, even years, so be patient. To clear blocked or partly blocked nasal passageways enough to take oxygen straight to the brain means that all the years of suppressed breathing have to be reversed. The thick white substance which has lined the respiratory tubes, because of undischarged nasal waste has to be melted into mucus, runny enough to be discharged via the orifices of the head, nose, mouth eyes, even ears! This can take quite a longish period.

The *melting* effect of correct oxygenation gradually dissolves the wax into a mucus sufficiently loose to be coughed up in the form of phlegm. This elimination process must take whatever time is required.

As a result we become aware of a gradual lightening in the breathing mechanism. It is as if we are beginning to *use* ourselves in a better way. We seem to be bringing in a new perspective in our loving respect for ourselves. We have more energy, confidence, an awareness of a sense regained from our childhood, that of the *joy* of life with which we were born. This has been lost or mislaid in our intellectual and materialistic culture, and we are now reclaiming our spiritual inheritance. The right use of breath (spirit) respiritualises us.

My own process of this rediscovery has been further confirmed in my breathing therapy sessions with clients who had been forced to use mouth breathing as a back-up because their nasal passages were almost blocked.

It is distressing to be with someone who cannot sustain nasal inhalation and exhalation for more than a few breaths, without having to open the mouth to draw in extra oxygen.

Living examples of being unable to use Nature's law for life, which cannot be disobeyed without eventual loss of health.

The frightening number of people who suffer from sinus problems, and who are dependent upon medication to clear, but probably damage, the delicate membrane lining of the nose, are proof of this appalling problem in our midst. From those I have met, their long-standing mental and emotional symptoms include constant worry, under-achievement, poor relationships, negative thought patterns, and general health problems. The one constant symptom was inhibited nostril breathing.

I vividly recall a key-speaker at a health conference many years ago, speaking of sinus problems as 'blocked tears'. A truism prevalent in all stratas of society, as the symptom of blocked breathing, the precursor of the blocked tears stalks our streets. *The tears are always those of the child within.*

Time and again as a person re-established correct nasal use, there was a noticeable reduction in stress symptoms, and an increasing ability and insight into ways to solve their difficulties *without my help*! Nothing else had happened other than the re-training of the breathing instinct and correct nasal use, which led them to solve their own problems.

I remember learning about the five basic instincts as a school-child. The one attributed to the nose was 'smell'. Why breathing for life was not taught us as the prime nose use I do not know. Surely smell is the *secondary* use of the nose.

Re-training in correct nasal breathing, which warms the air and catches dust before it reaches the sensitive membranes of the lungs, draws up a more adequate supply of oxygen to the brain, and in exhaling through the nose, we seem to excrete a more refined volume of waste CO_2 from the base of the lungs. Once again, try it and see. Stand easy, breathe in and out through the mouth, and then try the same action through the nose. Different as chalk from cheese.

If you have not been in the habit of using the nose properly, it may be a little difficult at first. As you bring lazy nasal muscles into use again, the result resembles trimming the hedges of an over-grown lane, which has restricted human access for some years!

A better intake of oxygen, opens up brain-cell information, which needs that extra sparkle of oxygen to open up new life, just as a plant sends out fresh green shoots. As Karen Roon says in *The New Way to Relax*, "like giving water to a dying daffodil". You notice this particularly when you are assisting a child in improved breathing.

As you become more nose aware, try watching the people on TV who are speaking, discussing or trying to answer questions in the various programmes. You may observe them (a) rubbing the ends of their noses as they give an indication of worry, (b) tapping the side of the nose as a sign of keeping something secret, and (c) taking the top of the nose between finger and thumb in trying to work out a problem. Over the years, like the hands and feet which are the outposts of the physical body, I have realised that the nose is really an outpost of the connection of the lungs with the brain and our feelings. Rubbing the tip signals a degree of worry, tapping the side seems to trigger a breath-hold in the diaphragm area, a holding-in, (of a secret) and the slight squeezing of the top of the nose, indicates trying to solve a problem, drawing answers from the intuitive right brain.

Some writers refer to this area at the top-centre of the nose between the eyes as the 'third eye'.

The tip of the nose does, I believe, have a direct connection to the lowest area of the lungs, which when filled correctly, stimulates what is known as the sacral (sacred?) area or *second brain*, the seat of wisdom and feeling, between the pelvic bone and the navel.

When this occurs, the up-rise of the breath from that lower point oxygenates the higher brain area, a strategic ignition activator for the harmony of mind/body/spirit.

I began to think that each tiny part of the nose has a connection with a specific part of the lungs and brain, and right use triggers infinite possibilities to fresh ideas and creative ways to use our potential. Something I would like to study more fully.

For me the most inspiring factor which has emerged from all this has been the emergence of my own and a client's spirituality. This has nothing to do with any religion, but a sure knowledge and acceptance of a Power greater than our own, which can be trusted. This awareness gives us the insight and courage to resolve former apparently insolvable life problems.

I seem to have spent quite a lot of time in the last years in the occupation of *musing,* which is perhaps an under-rated word. When did you last use it? It's not one I use very often, but it describes a period of silent communication with the self. No doubt all creativity arises from a period of musing.

When someone is stretched out nice and warm and comfortable, breathing away steadily, I sometimes cast a detached look at them, and realise that at a very deep level they are involved in an intense inner search. I believe that person is *re-inspiring* themselves as inspiring levels of their persona are revealed to them through the re-oxygenation of brain cells through correct breathing, which have held important core information now being restored to consciousness.

Have you ever observed someone whose nostrils are not equal, in that one side seems more open than the other? The narrower the nostril, the narrower the outlook. Wide nostrils I understand indicate a person of rude health, but of course there's a happy medium. Too wide can indicate a coarseness of outlook. When you observe a disparity of nostril width, It indicates that we are drawing up less oxygen up one side.

Remember the left nostril feeds the right creative brain, and the right nostril the left logical outgoing side. I have noticed that a number of correct breathing sessions seems to help re-balance the size of the nostril width, which also assists in re-balancing the two brain hemispheres.

Disparity in nostril width can mean over-stimulation of one brain hemisphere at the expense of the other.

To me learning the subtle language of the breath and nose has revealed as much information about the nature of man as the *Encyclopedia Britannica*!

The clients who come to us teach us so much, I am eternally grateful for the amazing insights imparted to me by people, some of whom I have now known for many years. You cannot teach what you do not really believe yourself. Much of what I have learned has come to me from what I can only call the People's University of Health, which is the wisdom already unconsciously known to us all, but so rarely imparted through our established centres of learning which ignore its vital educational importance.

I believe it is the old wisdom which we all know, which if it came into being, would regenerate the race and the world. Disease would become a rarity as Ramaharaka said. In ignoring the old wisdom, the medics and scientists have lost the way, and if we listen to them, mankind will never reach his potential, which has to be his spiritual potential *never mind if there's life or not on Mars!*

You hear of scientific experiments using stem cells from the lining of the nose which seems to affirm, without telling us why, that there must be something special about those cells, linked to our primary essence. Running the oxygen over them correctly must have very specific implications for our health as we breathe correctly, or incorrectly.

For me the science of the nose carries with it the full development of instinct, intuition, and the harvesting of the power of the creative brain. I am positive that as animals have a full range of sensitivity from the use of the organ of the nose, so humanity has probably lost the function of that same area of sensitivity by an insensitivity which veils from our awareness much that would delight our days.

At the beginning of this chapter I mentioned the work of three writers. In *The Science of Breath*, Ramacharaka refers to an outbreak of small-pox on a naval vessel. Of the deaths which resulted, all were mouth breathers, and not a single man who breathed correctly through the nose died.

If this assessment was applied in connection with the scourge of modern day diseases, I wonder what the researchers would find. What about MRSA? Swine flu?

In his book *The Healing Power of Breath*, Jonathan Daemion refers to the fact that nostril breathing stimulates the sinus cavities on its way to the brain, and a special essence within the air then stimulates certain areas of the brain into higher consciousness.

If we breathe out through the mouth, this consciousness is diminished, so that any shadowy impulse received via the brain is unlikely to be transformed into action. Since all action is the result of what we believe to be true from our consciousness, we have the choice by correct breathing as to whether our actions stem from a higher or lower impulse!

Tania Clifton Webb's very much up-to-date book on breathing, called *Breathe to Succeed In Every Aspect of Your Life* has made an enormously valuable contribution to the effect of correct breathing on our modern life-styles.

The title of her second chapter is called, as I mentioned earlier, 'The Nose - The Body's Second-best kept Secret' (*Breathing* is the first). What a great title. It refers to the fact that mouth breathing is an inefficient gas exchange, and she states that nose breathing increases oxygen intake by ten to twenty per cent.

The brain needs well over thirty-five per cent of the oxygen we take in (some say more). When correct, the process of exhalation excretes seventy per cent of our waste material in the form of gas. This excretory process is meant to be via the nostrils. I believe, although do not have documentary proof, that there is an area at the back of the throat over which the exhaled air has to pass, which acts as a '*catalytic converter*' and performs a purification function, in the same way that a filter by the same name on the exhaust pipe of a car reduces toxic fumes.

The incorrectly filtered toxic breath waste from the lungs carries infection, as it is a pollutant, which contaminates, and is probably the biggest carrier of infection in our hospitals. How many decades do we have to go through before all health-workers have to pass a breath-test? Health and Safety officers take note? Try it for yourselves!

So you have the choice between carnal or spiritual breathing.

BE AS NOSEY AS YOU LIKE ABOUT THE NOSE, IT WILL PAY YOU DIVIDENDS BEYOND PRICE.

Testimonials from people who have benefited through using Correct Breathing

When I was with a very sick elderly relative who had been on a series of antibiotic treatments for an infection which had entered their chests, I noticed that she was no longer using her nose but was instead using her mouth to breathe, her mouth had became her nose in breathing terms. I know that mouth breathing dries the airways and throat. The next thing to go was her swallow. This was tragic as she was not able to take in any liquids or nutrition via her mouth and had to be fed on liquids and sugar intravenously. My relative was never again able to eat because of the lost swallow and passed away within a couple of weeks. At various times I had tried to persuade her to use her nose to breathe but think that the nasal passage had become completely blocked through years of lack of use. I have noticed this pattern of breathing occurring in many elderly sick people, and believe that if they had known about the importance of using their nose to breathe and had practised regular nose breathing, their lives could have been extended by many years. The quality of their latter years would also have been improved.

A Correct Breathing Practitioner

I feel that my nose has cleared and I can breathe more easily. Practising my breathing exercises has helped a lot. I also feel less stressed. Thank you.

Mother of two young children

I feel so much more relaxed now, I had not known that breathing was so important.

When I first began to breathe as shown I could feel the tension around my shoulders but that has gone now.

My nose was quite blocked to begin with, but it cleared as I kept on with my breathing.

I had not realised that I could breathe up to the top of my lungs.

Comments made by participants in a short
introduction to Breathing Session

Breathing out through the mouth is accompanied by thinking negative thoughts. The positive thought which happened with this mouth breathing occurrence is that negative thinking always bring back negative returns, and that of course is a waste of time. This most important thought about mouth breathing being wrong occurred as I emerged from the M8 motorway into the city centre. I breathed out through my mouth quite strongly but at the same time a very important realisation came to me. I was also experiencing and internalising a powerful negative thought about a current situation. I am sure this change happened as part of my individual process of breath correction, that in breathing through my mouth I was going against nature's laws. It was certainly a pivotal moment or I would not now remember it so vividly.

Woman remembering an event connected with breathing

* * *

Excerpts from Student Essays

GREAT BIG TRUST, LEVEL 7 INTRODUCTION TO CORRECT BREATHING COURSE

Mental and emotional health are also deeply connected to the breath. It has been accepted for some time now that emotional memory is stored in the soft tissues of the body rather than in the memory banks of the brain. A poor and inadequate respiratory pattern will ensure that unresolved and unconscious emotional issues and traumas remain locked into the body, causing all kinds of physical symptoms, ranging from muscular tensions and chronic aches and pains, stiffness, frozen shoulders and arthritis, to cancers and life-threatening illness and disease.

Bernadette

What other Visionary Writers have said about Breathing and Life

Mouth breathing dries the airways. Slouching restricts the diaphragm.

Dinah Bradley and Tania Clifton-Smith, Breathing Works for Asthma

If your nose is blocked you will start mouth-breathing. The problem with mouth-breathing is that it allows cool, dry, unfiltered air into the lungs – a little like rubbing sandpaper over your skin. This causes irritation which can lead to asthma.

The mouth is there for emergencies. We know that when we mouth-breath quickly this has a direct link to our autonomic nervous system, triggering the sympathetic 'flight and fight' branch that readies us for emergencies.

Dinah Bradley and Tania Clifton-Smith, Breathing Works for Asthma

Since air enters the body with each *in*-breath, we can look to the process of breathing in – or *in*spiration – to find the key which will unlock this magical puzzle.

As air is drawn in through the nose, it passes down through the windpipe (the trachea) and eventually flows into the lungs. It is in the lungs that the *gross-Air* energies are utilised: oxygen is taken up by the red blood cells and carbon dioxide (CO_2) is discharged directly into the lungs. This process of *oxygenating* the body and washing it clean of waste gases (like CO_2, carbon monoxide, etc) is amazing enough in itself!

On the way to the trachea, however, there is a time when the Air flows past – or, in some cases, only *near* – various openings or 'empty holes' in the bony structure of the head. There are eight of these holes in every person's head and these empty places are called the *cranial sinuses* or simply the 'sinus cavities'.

Western medicine does not yet understand how the sinuses function in relation to the *subtle-Air* energies, and relates to them in a negative sense as a means by which the body is supposedly 'trying' to minimise the weight of the head! This notion suggests that we are 'stuck with' bigger heads than we need, so our bodies grow with holes in the superstructure of the skull to keep the weight down! How preposterous! And... how presumptuous we are!

Now even though such blindly self-limiting concepts *can* and *do* affect each of our self-images and program our perceptions of how things work as we live in these complex human bodies, we also know that we can open ourselves directly to a more *wholistic experience* of the reality of things by – among other ways – simply breathing. Like this:

As you draw Breath into your body through your nose, air naturally flows through or past (or near) these open sinuses and some of the most subtle energies of the Air penetrate these cavities and there *discharges* (energy) directly into your brain!

Jonathan Daemion, The Healing Power of Breath

The breathing mechanism of Man is so constructed that he may breathe either through the mouth or nasal tubes, but it is a matter of vital importance to him which method he follows, as one brings health and strength and the other disease and weakness.

Yogi Ramacharaka, The Hindu-Yogi Science of Breath

Many of the diseases to which civilised man is subject are undoubtedly caused by this common habit of mouth-breathing. Children permitted to breathe in this way grow up with impaired vitality and weakened constitutions, and in manhood and woman-hood break down and become chronic invalids. The mother of the savage race does better, being evidently guided by her intuition. She seems to instinctively recognise that the nostrils are the proper channels for the conveyance of air to the lungs, and she trains her infant to close its little lips and breathe through the nose. She tips its head forward when it is asleep, which closes the lips and makes nostril-breathing imperative. If our civilised mothers were to adopt the same plan, it would work a great good for the race.

Many contagious diseases are contracted by the disgusting habit of mouth-breathing, and many cases of cold and catarrhal afflictions are also attributable to the same cause.

Yogi Ramacharaka, The Hindu-Yogi Science of Breath

An instance is related in which small-pox became epidemic on a warship in foreign parts, and every death which resulted was that of some sailor or marine who was a mouth-breather, not a single nostril-breather succumbing.

Yogi Ramacharaka, The Hindu-Yogi Science of Breath

* * *

The intricate purifying organization of the nostrils, arresting and holding the impure particles in the air, is as important as is the action of the mouth in stopping cherry-stones and fish-bones and preventing them from being carried on to the stomach.

Man should no more breathe through his mouth than he would attempt to take food through his nose.

Yogi Ramacharaka, The Hindu-Yogi Science of Breath

Pingala is the dynamic male principle and ida the passive female principle. The left brain hemisphere operates on the same principle as pingala. It processes information logically, sequentially, and functions according to time sequence. The right hemisphere is concerned with intuition, mental creativity and orientation in space. When both nostrils operate simultaneously the energy is being transferred from one hemisphere to the other. It passes through a thin sheet of membrane between the two hemispheres called the corpus callosum. At this time the whole brain can function and perception will not be limited to one mode of processing.

Swami Saraswati [trans], Hatha Yoga Pradipika

The most radical part of learning to nose-breathe again was I could kiss properly. My boyfriend pointed out to me that kissing me used to be like kissing a gasping goldfish. And it's made the rest of my sex life so much better too, because I feel so much better. I hadn't realised what I was missing out on.

Dinah Bradley, Hyperventilation Syndrome

* * *

Inspirational quotes to help on your Breathing Journey

Whatever you do or dream you can do - begin it.
Boldness has genius and power and magic in it.

Johann Goethe

Our doubts are traitors and make us lose the good we oft
might win by fearing to attempt.

Shakespeare

It is the difficulties that show what men are.

Epictetus

A man with outward courage dares to die
A man with inward courage dares to live.

Lao-Tzu

The beginning is the most important part of the work.

Plato

Every child is born a genius.

Albert Einstein

* * *

PART FIVE

The Abdomen and the Solar Plexus

A healthy baby is the perfect instructor in breathing and
relaxation. Watch it and see why. The new-born child uses all the
muscles of its trunk that should be involved in the breathing
process, those of the abdomen, sides and back.

Karin Roon

A HEALTHY SMALL CHILD demonstrates the proper use of the
body in tandem with the proper use of breathing. It will be seen
that the expansion of its body with each inhale starts from a point
between the pelvic bone and the naval. It is said that this power
point of the human body is also the source of the auto-immune
system and that correct breathing constantly re-stimulates this area
as an over-riding energy source which can fight infection. Incorrect
breathing which weakens this process means that lung expansion
avoids the use of this vital power source, and is therefore the prime
reason as to why we become vulnerable to infection.

When the proper expansion of the lungs from the lower belly
takes place, and the air moves through the lungs, it then stimulates
the solar plexus, which emanates from the gut and is known as
the 'sun of the body'. Thus the *'starting'* mechanism is the lower
abdomen and the *'accelerator'* is the solar plexus.

When someone breathes correctly from the lower abdomen
there is a strong muscular reaction from this point. If an individual
is under constant fear and stress this muscular plexus is soft
and spongy, anxiety and tension becoming a dominant factor,
weakening the muscular reaction. It is said that such a person
has 'no guts'. The french physiotherapist, Pierre Pallardy amply
develops these ideas in his book *Gut Instinct*.

It has been noticed that in people who develop obesity, the lower gut area is invariably weak. Possibly the obesity and an ineffective comfort stop of food intake, is a compensatory defence mechanism. R. D. Laing, the former well-known Scottish psychologist, suggested that "breathing and the rhythm of the heart can be damaged, perhaps for life, by cutting or throttling the umbilical chord at birth while it and the placenta are still functionally us".

Pierre Pallardy, refers to the lower gut area as the abdominal brain, suggesting that this area is our emotional centre. Vivian Ryder wrote about the vagus nerves as being 'the longest cranial nerves in the body, stretching from deep within our brain stem right down to the gut, provide a powerful communication cable between our head brain and our gut brain', transporting the 'life force' between the two brains and around the body.

If physical exercise and sport of any kind does not promote correct breathing from the gut area it is likely to cause us more harm than good in the long term. Proper physical activity must stimulate the abdominal and solar plexus area in order to activate the strong active energy of the life force which needs to flow throughout the body to ensure physical, mental and emotional health. Many famous sports people die at an early age from life-threatening illness often caused by the imbalance of holding tension whilst pushing the body past its limits. Our devotion and admiration for the word 'sport' does not necessarily ensure the longevity which consistently is achieved by correct breathing.

People from the East are more aware of the importance of what they call the 'hara' in linking the lower and upper brains to achieve balance. It is said that the heart contains more brain cells that the brain itself!

The lack of communication between the lower and upper brains through incorrect breathing, is one of the most obvious causes of sexual dysfunction. In the absence of correct breathing the repression of such a powerful urge leads to perverted ways of satisfying such a strong sexual drive because there is no healthy conversion of this energy in a healthy creative way. Paedophilia probably arises from this perversion. Correcting the respiratory function and establishing harmony between the two brains could be an important aspect in the treatment of this condition, and part of the corrective regime where jail sentences are involved. Research has proven that punishment alone does not prevent reoccurrence.

A protruding gut or belly, whilst obviously a common symptom of over indulgence in eating and alcohol, still indicates a block between the two brains, (the gut and the head) and has a knock on strain on the heart, which is the seat of love and compassion, and may have been damaged in childhood from unloving nurturing methods. Conversely, the acute 'pulling in' of the pelvic area of the lower gut, which women mistakenly accept in order to become fashion icons, again means that the vital link between the upper and lower, or emotional and intellectual brains has been disconnected. This often leads to the 'baby doll' sexual symbol of the 'girl woman'.

Whenever there is a block which prevents the healthy self-love which is generated from a close communication via correct breathing, between the lower brain, the gut, and the upper brain, the head, there will be a need for a compensatory 'feel good' factor. The over use of material sustenance, over-eating, as a compensatory urge suggests an addictive solace to be found in food. Once the two brains are re-connected, our natural 'feel good' factor re-asserts itself and the use of food resumes its natural function as an energiser in taking appropriate physical and spiritual action in the world.

The suppression of correct breathing from the belly or lower abdomen also suppresses the intuitive instinct which can only come into its own power when it is activated and released through correct breathing. Unless our lives are dictated to and in touch with the intuitive instinct we are apt to feel thoroughly dissatisfied by the way we seem to attract misfortune. We blame 'life' for our problems, ignoring the fact that the solution lies in touching base with our intuitive faculty so strong in childhood. Life then becomes a joyful dance.

* * *

Show me how a man breathes and I will tell you what kind of a man he is.

Ancient quote

The healthy man breathes from his big toe, the sick man from his throat.

Chinese quote

The re-connection, by correct breathing, of the lower emotional gut and the upper intellectual brain enables the truth of the following lines to become a reality:

Truth is within ourselves; it takes no rise
From outward things, whate'er you may believe.
There is an inmost centre in us all,
Where truth abides in fulness; and around,
Wall upon wall, the gross flesh hems it in,
This perfect, clear perception - which is truth.
A baffling and perverting carnal mesh
Binds it, and makes all error: and to KNOW,
Rather consists in opening out a way
Whence the imprisoned splendour may escape,
Than in effecting entry for a light
Supposed to be without.

Robert Browning, from 'Paracelsus'

* * *

Testimonials from people who have benefited through using Correct Breathing

Learning to breathe and relax played a pivotal part in a young woman conceiving naturally after several years of unsuccessful IVF treatment.

Great Big Trust

I have suffered bad migraine headaches ever since childhood. These headaches were particularly bad during my period times. Someone told me about correct breathing and I sought out a person who could teach me how to breathe correctly to help reduce my migraine headaches, I was not disappointed, and can now say that my migraine headaches are now a very rare occurrence and my general health is much better through using correct breathing. Thank you.

Woman artist

I am a thirty eight year old woman living in the Glasgow area with my husband and daughter. I have suffered from asthma from about the age of three and regularly took inhalers to control this. I have experienced bouts of depression and anxiety since about the age of eighteen, the most severe of which led to a stay in hospital. I was prescribed various medications but never felt that they had any great effect on my symptoms. Despite this I fought my way back to a reasonable quality of life. I began a part time college course but was often prone to overwhelming episodes of anxiety. A tutor at college recommended that I arrange a meeting with someone she knew who taught Correct Breathing. I arranged an appointment but had minimal expectations and was unconvinced that anything could make a significant impact on the way I was feeling.

I began a course of Corrective Breath Work in January. During the sessions I was required to lie on a mat in a prone position and covered with a blanket for comfort. I would follow spoken instructions which indicated the depth and rate of the breath. The sessions gradually increased in length over a six week period. As a treatment it is non-invasive and gives back control of the breath to the client. For me it was the catalyst to my recovery. It allowed me to realise that there were areas of my life which I could control effectively and provided me with a very powerful tool to use in times of stress. I had a regular repeat prescription for ventolin inhalers. They are no longer registered as a repeat item for me, and in the last six months I have used them only once. Correct Breathing is a simple process which is easily called upon in times of stress. It has an added bonus of being deeply relaxing.

Getting back in touch with my breath and my breathing has been an invaluable experience in my life.

Young Glasgow woman

Limited shallow breathing has been proved to lead to insomnia, constipation, poor digestion, lack of confidence, depression, fatigue, high blood pressure, panic attacks, poor performance in exams and poor concentration, weakened immune system, floating anxiety, addictions, bad and abusive relationships, work place bullying, depression and suicidal tendencies, mood swings, ageing allergies. We have proved that correcting the breathing pattern changes all of the above.

The Great Big Trust

* * *

Excerpts from Student Essays

GREAT BIG TRUST, LEVEL 7 INTRODUCTION TO CORRECT BREATHING COURSE

Eastern philosophies such as yoga and Buddhism are aware of energy pathways throughout and surrounding the body. With the correct breath, energy pathways rise up from the solar plexus (in the abdomen between the navel and the pelvic bone) to the opening of the 'crown chakra' which represents a higher or spiritual consciousness. We begin to see that we are unique in our own set of blueprints that determine who we are but that we also have a contribution to the world we live in. A set of truths that we want to live by that are loving and are given to us intuitively from this unseen source.

Karen

What other Visionary Writers have said about Breathing and Life

The Solar Plexus, or Abdominal Brain, the functions and offices, the powers and activities, of which constitute the chief subject matter of this book, is, as the name indicated, situated in the abdomen. Some of its filaments, however, accompany the branches of the aorta (the great artery) which are distributed to the stomach, intestines, spleen, pancreas, liver, and certain other organs, but not to the lungs. It is situated in the upper part of the abdomen, behind the stomach, in front of the aorta or great artery, and in front of the pillars of the diaphragm. Its place is popularly known as 'the pit of the stomach' or back of the point where the ribs begin to separate and spread to each side.

The Solar Plexus is the great plexus, i.e., network of nerve-fibres, mass of nerve-substance, etc., of the great Sympathetic Nervous

System. It is composed of both grey and white substance, or brain-matter, similar to that of the other brains of Man. It receives and distributes nerve-impulses and currents to all of the abdominal organs, and supplies the main organs of nutrition, assimilation, etc., with their nervous energy. It performs most important offices in the so-called 'vegetative life' of the body, supplying the nerve-energy which is required for the processes of nutrition, assimilation growth, etc. In fact, it is the great power-house of physical life-energy. The bodily functions cannot be performed without it; when it is injured the entire physical well-being is at once seriously affected; and when it receives a severe shock, death often ensues, a fact which the history of prize-fighting amply illustrates.

Its name, 'solar', was bestowed upon it by reason of (1) its central position; (2) the fact that its filaments extend in all directions to the important abdominal organs, like the rays of the sun; and (3) the fact that it is recognised as being the power-house, and great reservoir of 'life-force', just as the sun is the great power-house and reservoir of material energy of our solar system.

Theron Q. Dumont, The Solar Plexus or Abdominal Brain

A writer has stated that if the air cells of the lungs were spread out over an unbroken surface, they would cover an area of fourteen thousand square feet.

The air is drawn into the lungs by the action of the diaphragm, a great, strong, flat, sheet-like muscle, stretched across the chest, separating the chest-box from the abdomen. The diaphragm's action is almost as automatic as that of the heart, although it may be transformed into a semi-voluntary muscle by an effort of the will. When it expands, it increases the size of the chest and lungs, and the air rushes into the vacuum thus created. When it relaxes, the chest and lungs contract and the air is expelled from the lungs.

Yogi Ramacharaka, The Hindu-Yogi Science of Breath

For a start, it is worth noting that the lungs are placed between the other great organs of the body. They share their cavity, the thorax, with the heart on either side of which their peaks lie; and though there is no great connection between the two there is strong evidence that, just as lung *disease* can certainly lead to heart disease, so bad use of the lungs can lead to the heart behaving badly. One mechanism which has been suggested for this fact is that deep breathing creates a partial vacuum round the heart and its nearby blood-vessels and so enables them to expand properly, whilst at the same time the heart muscles themselves are well fed with oxygenated blood. It is also known that the diaphragm acts as an auxiliary pump helping the blood on its last lap back to the heart. And the *use* of our lungs is something over which we have more control than their actual *size*, which has been proved to be closely related to proneness to coronary thrombosis.

An American physician, indeed, recently published a paper in which he announced that he had found deep breathing beneficial in coronary conditions in an experience lasting over more than a decade, enabling him often to dispense with the use of drugs and vasodilators.

William P. Knowles, New Life Through Breathing

Negative thoughts weigh heavily on the abdomen and disrupt its proper functioning. The body is isolated from the mind and the rupture between the two brains is total.

The plain fact of the matter is that most people do not breathe correctly. The majority of adults and, without exception, every adolescent I encounter in the course of my daily practice breathes to only about 50 per cent of their capacity.

Social pressures are to blame for this loss of natural breathing capacity. In early childhood, up to the age of two years or so, when consciousness of 'self' and the external world begins to manifest itself, children fill their lungs and abdomen with air – and empty both in a similar fashion. Later, when the pressures of the outside world come into play – introducing emotions such as stress, anxiety, timidity – the respiratory rhythm accelerates and the initial natural and spontaneous practice of deep breathing gives way to 'social' breathing, which is less deep and confined to the lungs and the bronchial tubes (and, even there, is only partial). As a result, the volume of air ingested into the body is reduced by approximately half.

We have become accustomed to *not* breathing with our abdomen. For several reasons, this is nothing short of catastrophic.

First and foremost, it is catastrophic for the abdomen itself. When it doesn't get enough oxygen, the abdomen becomes sluggish and underperforms. This invites the onset of disorders such as colitis, constipation and stomach cramps. Problems absorbing food and eliminating waste materials lead to exhaustion, insomnia, nervous tension, weight gain, sexual dysfunction, allergies and many other debilitating conditions.

Pierre Pallardy,
Gut Instinct - What your stomach is trying to tell you

That the Solar Plexus, or Abdominal Brain, should be able to exercise an important influence and power over the Health and Vitality of the individual is perceived immediately when we realise its relation to the organs performing the important functions of life. The Solar Plexus, as you have seen, is the great central storehouse of nervous energy, or 'life-force', of the physical body. It sends to this organ, and to that gland, the supply of nervous energy and vital force which is necessary to animate and energise those parts of the body, and the other parts adjacent thereto.

To understand the importance of this nervous energy or vital force which is controlled and dispensed by the Solar Plexus, it is necessary only to consider the activities performed by means of its power. For instance, we find that the processes of digestion, assimilation, nutrition and elimination are possible only when the supply of vital force is sufficient. Likewise, we find that the processes of the circulation of the blood are dependent upon the supply of the vital force.

Theron Q. Dumont, The Solar Plexus or Abdominal Brain

The lymphatic duct travels alongside the spine at the back of the thoracic cage. Movement of this region is crucial for circulation within the lymphatic system – as this regulates our immune system it is a very important function. A good breathing pattern will move the fluid in a regular, rhythmical way. Irregular patterns may cause the fluid to stagnate, leading to health problems.

Tania Clifton-Smith, Breathe To Succeed

Your diaphragm Helps Too. The diaphragm forms a kind of partition between the lungs and the other organs of the body, like a movable ceiling. Below it are the stomach, kidneys, intestines, sex organs, and bladder. Therefore, when the diaphragm moves – like a kind of suction cup – with each expansion of the lungs, the organs below it are exposed to a soft pressure which acts as a stimulation. If the breathing is shallow and the diaphragm moves only slightly, all the vital organs that depend for their proper functioning on this stimulation begin to suffer in their own functions. Constipation, stomach, gall-bladder, and kidney trouble are frequently a result of lack of proper function. Therefore, it becomes apparent that complete breathing plays a vital and essential part in our general health, and that its impairment can have widespread results.

Nor are the lower organs the only ones affected by a poorly functioning diaphragm. This muscle plays a large part in assisting the heart with its work. When the diaphragm does little work, the whole burden falls upon the heart, providing yet another reason for the increase of heart trouble. And here we return again to a result of our contemporary living conditions. Nothing makes it more difficult for the diaphragm to keep up its stimulating influence on the inner organs than our sixteen-hour habit of sitting.

Karin Roon, The New Way to Relax

Every human being is born with his own personal rhythm, as distinctive and individual as his finger-prints. Whether, as doctors assume, this rhythm is dictated largely by the glands, is unimportant for our purpose. What *is* important is that each human being should learn to be aware of his own rhythm and live in accordance with it.

This personal rhythm is physical, mental, and emotional. When it is thrown off balance, the whole system suffers, mentally and emotionally as well as physically. For the human being cannot be separated into air-tight compartments; a physical body, a mind, the emotions. These three are so inter-related that it is impossible to consider them separately.

Karin Roon, The New Way to Relax

We know the effect on the motor of faulty rhythm and the wrong speed. The dials of motor-cars turn red as a warning when the speed is pushed over fifty miles an hour. The nervous system sends out its warning signals when our rhythms go wrong, but we either ignore the signals or fail to understand what they are telling us.

Karin Roon, The New Way to Relax

Mind and Body Much of mental illness is a result of lack of harmony between feeling and thinking. The mind loses control because an emotion such as unhappiness or loneliness or fear has been too overpowering; or because, in an attempt to escape from these realities, people withdraw so far into a world of fantasies that they cross the border of insanity. One of nature's best regulating forces for the balance of mind and emotions is the process of physical breathing.

Karin Roon, The New Way to Relax

Unfortunately, too little is known about the long term effects of insufficient breathing to be certain about the real consequences, but research indicates that a number of age-related illnesses are (partly at least) the effects of insufficient breathing. These conditions include; allergies, asthma, cancer, circulatory problems, diabetes, epilepsy, headaches and migraine, hypertension (often causing high blood pressure), peptic ulcers and sexual organ dysfunction.

Gunnel Minett, Exhale, An Overview of Breathwork

In his book *The Tao of Natural Breathing*, Dennis Lewis describes how different emotions have different breathing patterns. Anger has a short inhale and strong exhale (just like an angry bull). Anger also leads to tensed muscles, in particular in the neck, jaws, chest and hands. Fear has a short breathing pattern with fast and irregular breaths, leading to 'knots' in the stomach. Sadness has jerky, sobbing and superficial breathing patterns, which create a feeling of emptiness in the stomach. Impatience has a short, jerky and incoherent breathing pattern, which generates tensions in the chest. Guilt has a restricted, suffocating breathing pattern, leading to a feeling of heaviness in the whole body. Boredom has a short and lifeless breathing pattern, which creates the feeling that the whole body is lifeless. Positive emotions on the other hand – such as love, friendship and compassion are associated with a deep and comfortable breathing pattern and a feeling of openness and life-giving energy throughout the body.

Gunnel Minett, Exhale, An Overview of Breathwork

The main storage place for life energy in the body is in the area around the solar plexus, and this is also regarded as our emotional centre. The energy is mainly stored in the lower *Tan Tien* between the navel, kidneys and the upper part of the pubic bone. With a good supply of energy in this area it is easier to absorb energy in other forms. It acts as a kind of magnet that attracts energy from outside, by co-ordinating its vibrations with the surrounding world.

Gunnel Minett, Exhale, An Overview of Breathwork

* * *

Affirmations

AN AFFIRMATION IS A POSITIVE STATEMENT
OF ABSOLUTE TRUTH. REPEAT IT TO YOURSELF
OR WRITE IT OUT TO RE-AFFIRM SOMETHING
THAT YOU WANT TO BECOME TRUE.

*The door to my greater good is open wide,
and it is nailed back.*

Florence Scovel-Shinn

The sun never sets on my true desires.

The universe always says 'yes'.

It is now safe for me to listen to my intuition.

Being me suits everyone else.

Love is stronger than fear.

It is now safe for me to release my past with love.

*I am always in the right place at the right time
doing what is right for me.*

* * *

Inspirational quotes to help on your Breathing Journey

The only real valuable thing is intuition.
Albert Einstein

Imagination, not invention, is the supreme master of life.
Joseph Conrad

One of the simplest things about all the facts of life is that to get where you want to go, you must keep on keeping on.
Norman Vincent Peale

If love is the answer, could you tell me what the question was?
Lily Tomlin

Go confidently in the direction of your dreams. Act as though it were impossible to fail.
Dorothea Brandt

Life can be understood backwards; but it must be lived forwards.
Soren Kierkegaard

He who knows others is wise;
He who knows himself is enlightened
Lao Tzu

* * *

PART SIX

On Rest

IN THE DEVELOPMENT OF MAN through many thousands of years the power and greed principle reminds us that we are but a stone's throw from the days of the slave traders, the more recent slaves of the cotton mills of the industrial revolution and the present slaves of the computer world entombed in countless oxygen starved offices in concrete blocks, carrying out left brain dominated activity. If something isn't spiritual, it isn't. We still have a vast majority of the population who if questioned would say that they feel tired and lacked energy. Small children are denied a proper mid-day rest through the work demands of both parents, and little ones under eight involved in a 'work day' which often begins well before 8 am and finishes after 6 pm, when eventually collected by tired parents from after-school 'care'. During the ten hour working day of these small children very few are given the chance of a mid-day nap, essential to the young fledgling. Rest and recuperation is not recognised to be an important part of the routine of small children who we like to boast about as being 'always on the go'. Hyperactivity?

We train young people virtually from the pram upwards to feel that the only time we can legitimately take rest is when we actually go to bed, and we force ourselves past the fatigue point time and again. In doing so we damage the nervous system. Our thought process becomes out of harmony with nature, our principle governing body. As the smallest and weakest members of society, children are on the front line of our warfare with nature. The demonic rush and bustle of an inner-city centre vividly reveals a majority of people rushing fast to keep up with their internalised and relentless timetables.

Nature never rushes, her timetable dominates our lives whether recognised or not. Those who begin to breathe correctly and slow the hitherto life turmoil within, begin to see the foolishness of our present life-styles. A business man in charge of a Far-Eastern concern allowed his employees time during the day to rest when they felt fatigue became dominant. There was no drop in productivity, indeed it rose. Could this not be possible universally? Those who voice general doom and gloom as an end result need to try this first. A number of schools have begun relaxation and meditation classes in England and elsewhere. Teachers report an improvement in behaviour, creativity and classroom atmosphere.

Only stressed and closed minds reject such pioneering trends.

There is a saying "take rest, a field that is well rested yields a beautiful crop". Another writer states that when we are tired we see everything through emotional magnifying glasses (a breeding ground for stress and aggression)! When we learn to relax and breathe correctly, our emotional magnifying glasses cease to over emphasise the negative and restore the balance to the positive.

The poem below captures well the jarring effect pushing ourselves beyond weariness brings about:

> When our spirits meet old
> Weariness with his rust eaten knife,
> There is no corner of our house kept sweet,
> That is not trampled bloody.

As usual Shakespeare sums up beautifully the importance of rest:

> Sleep that knits up the ravell'd sleeve of care,
> The death of each day's life, sore labour's bath,
> Balm of hurt minds, great nature's second course,
> Chief nourisher in life's feast,

We do not deliberately over-tire and over-strain our beloved pet animals. Is it the strong puritanical and slave instinct still echoing down the ages that prevents us from giving courteous and sensible recognition that men, women and children are not machines but worthy of proper regard? If we obey the instinct to rest and 'top up our batteries' when they are over-charged, as individuals we would be much more likable, even lovable, collectively an enchanting species fit to raise children. Why are such inspiring and life supporting rest activities, involving only a few minutes daily, not universally accepted and included as part of the general school curriculum?

Healthy children almost always respond to their need for rest and will fall asleep, often on the instant, when they feel tired. It is not natural to push ourselves when we are tired, nor to take stimulants to keep ourselves going beyond fatigue. This will only build up ongoing levels of stress which will impair our ability to function, mentally, emotionally and physically and will eventually lead to illness and breakdown. Mike George in his book *Learn to Relax* says, "Restful sleep is vital for relaxation. Without it we force our minds and bodies to work against Nature, which can only lead to fatigue and greatly increased anxiety."

The media frequently informs us of heads of the financial and banking world and the giants of industry whose position in the commercial empire is destroyed because of proven revelations concerning unhealthy and socially offensive sexual practices and involvements with pornography and the exploitation of pornographic sexual behaviour. This excessive detrimental sexual behaviour contrasts with the sexual drives of a healthy individual. The over-dominance of wealth accumulation, power and control leads to an over-dominance of left brain activity, with limited functioning of the right creative brain. A block or imbalance is created, preventing normal healthy sexual functioning and leads to deep internal tension which requires a relief no longer obtainable through healthy sexual activity. This imbalance takes the individual further down the road of perverted sexual practices and moral degradation.

The foundations of the so called 'pillars of society' are dramatically turned to dust before the public gaze. The world-wide slave trade in the use of vulnerable young women in lewd sexual and harmful practices lowers the world's standards.

It does not have to be like this.

Testimonials from people who have benefited through using Correct Breathing

As you know, I have taught Science in Secondary Schools all my life - a difficult and demanding job at the best of times. In 36 years of teaching I have been acting Head of Department, Sixth Form College Tutor, and Team Leader responsible for a quarter of the pupils in one particular school. I strongly believe that I coped better because my breathing had been corrected by yourselves. It is amazing that breathing malfunctions so easily and at such an early age. I have found that most people breathe in 'panic mode' - shallow, tight breathing which tips them over into anger and tension at the drop of a hat. Such people will not fulfill their potential, let alone keep calm in their daily interactions. However, once readjusted it results in clearer thinking, increased confidence, more thoughtfulness, better sleep patterns, a decrease in 'nerves' brought on by exams, relationships, and so on. People need space to find themselves and this is what correct breathing will do. The list of benefits is endless.

Mary, senior teacher of biology

COMMENTS ON WORKSHOP HELD IN A VILLAGE HALL, NOVEMBER 2008

A wonderful workshop in which I feel I've learned a lot. I feel the benefit from breathing correctly, and am already looking forward to future events.

Helen

Very open and friendly meeting. Excellent to have the opportunity to attend such a workshop. Looking forward to reading more on your website and practicing with the breathing. Nice to have so much one-to-one time in a group.

Erica

Presence through breath entering the stillness. Your divine nature returning to the source.

David

Very interesting and thought-provoking afternoon. Thanks to everyone for their friendly support, and for sharing personal stories.

Georgie

Breathing correctly makes me feel stronger and walk taller. I always feel that I fill with energy when I breathe from my boots. It was a pleasure to meet you, and to confirm what I have felt for a long time.

Aimee, musician and music teacher

Excerpts from Student Essays

GREAT BIG TRUST, LEVEL 7 INTRODUCTION
TO CORRECT BREATHING COURSE

Spirit is breath, a connection with nature, a getting to know oneself and a balance of body, mind and spirit. If we are to function fully in all these areas we must ensure we have enough restful sleep, good nutrition, exercise, and pay attention to our breathing. Depriving ourselves of any or all of these things will lead to health problems because we are going against nature. Many sports people push themselves physically which often results in repetitive strain injuries. Likewise if we spend too much time straining our eyes reading or on the computer, overdoing mental work, our eyes will suffer, and require good rest to recover.

Carol

Incorrect breathing patterns will have had a negative, sometimes long held belief that we need to keep pushing ourselves too far, work too hard, too many long hours, so that we can buy more and more material things, go on more holidays etc. Instead of relaxing us, they will probably add to our stress levels, preventing us from enjoying these things because our minds are too busy trying to work out how we will obtain the extra money we need to pay for these things, for which we may have got into debt, and so, onwards we continue on the 'merry go round'!

Marion

What other Visionary Writers have said about Breathing and Life

The energy of life is is always at Alpha, which is a restful rhythm.

Mike George, Learn to Relax

Finding time to relax is just as important as making time to exercise. Research carried out in America shows that keeping constantly on the go not only predisposes you to headaches, fatigue and 'stress' illnesses like heart disease, but also lowers blood levels of the antibodies that protect you from infection and disease. Simply practicing relaxation, however, reduces suscepti-bility to stress illnesses and can get the antibody levels up again. The more you relax, the higher the levels climb.

Relaxing completely, not just slumping in front of the television, rarely comes naturally, so a relaxing technique is essential. Once you've learned the difference between being unnecessarily tense and appropriately relaxed, you should have the habit for life. A recent British study found that people given training in muscle relaxation and deep breathing not only developed markedly lower blood pressures than a control group, but because they had incorporated the technique into their daily lives, they maintained their healthier, relaxed lifestyles after the study without further prompting.

Relaxation CDs are a good way to get started. They force you to stop, listen and learn to relax completely. You may get irritated by hearing the same thing over and over, but once you've mastered the technique, you can jettison the tape and use music, the radio or silence to help you release the tension in your body and empty your mind of traumas past and possible.

From 'Here's Health' magazine

CHANGE YOUR LIFE BY DOING NOTHING

A Church of England Bishop, the Rev. Stephen Cottrell, Bishop of Reading, has written a book called *Do Nothing to Change Your Life*. A spokesman said: "Bishop Stephen is urging the country to discover what happens when we simply stop and rest, in a passionate plea for the nation to ditch endless 'to do' lists, constant streams of emails and an increasingly 24/7 culture."

The Bishop is urging Britons to schedule in a daily 'happy hour' when televisions and radios are switched off. He also advocates 'lengthy lie-ins'.

In his book he argues that taking time out can lead to "an adventure of self-discovery and creativity".

He criticises time-saving devices, arguing that all they achieve is added expectations upon individuals to cram more into each day.

He said: "By learning to sit still, slow down, by discerning when to shut up and when to speak out, you learn to travel through life differently. There is new delight and purpose in the mundane and the ordinary things of life. Making tea becomes a treat, traveling to work an adventure."

* * *

Parental Messages

Did you get any of these messages from your parents? If you did, correcting your breathing will help to cancel out their negative effect. There are many more messages which you may have received and which are still having a negative effect on your life. Breathe them out and let them go forever. Create your own positive messages and affirmations for yourself. You are beautiful, complete and whole.

You dope.

You are unloveable.

I'll pay more attention to you if you are bad
than if you are good.

Think the way I tell you to think.

I won't pay any attention to you, no matter what you do.

Affirmations

AN AFFIRMATION IS A POSITIVE STATEMENT
OF ABSOLUTE TRUTH. REPEAT IT TO YOURSELF
OR WRITE IT OUT TO RE-AFFIRM SOMETHING
THAT YOU WANT TO BECOME TRUE.

It is now safe for me to surrender into rest.

It is now safe for me to honour other people's need for rest.

Rest is never time wasted, it is time saved

Answers come to me when I rest

Solutions come to me when I rest

In rest is my health

Flowers never chatter, in their stillness is their charm.

Inspirational quotes to help on your Breathing Journey

Be Still and know that I am God.

The Bible

Consider the Lilies of the field, they toil not
neither do they reap.

The Bible

A clear conscience is the best pillow

Old Saying

The knowledge of work well done gives us music at midnight

Saying

All shall be well, and all manner of things shall be well

Julian of Norwich

It is a sin to ignore our need for rest,
we automatically go past our best.

Great Big Trust

To maximise your brain potential, rest it.

Great Big Trust

I can't wait to go to bed with God. (Thinking that the
restful time before sleep is like being with God)

Lilla Bek

It is only when we are resting and at peace with ourselves
that our guides and our helpers can speak to us, so that even
the silence is pregnant with possibility.

Lilla Bek

Simplify!

Henry David Thoreau

* * *

PART SEVEN

Relationships

THE FOLLOWING SECTION on relationships must lead to a final conclusion that our first and most important relationship is with ourselves, whatever the dynamics of our upbringing, present relationships and involvements. Later in this book we refer to the magnetic frequency of the earth's electrical field as being constantly maintained at alpha rhythm, i.e. 15-25 cycles per second; this is the loving frequency of alpha. Self corrective breathing therefore restores not only our loving relationship with ourselves, but also with that of the earth, or nature.

Theodore Roszak in his book, *The Voice Of The Earth* observed that our deepest relationship is not with our parents but with nature:

> There is no mental health in our cities until we reawaken our psychic links with Nature, suggesting that our very earliest sub-conscious awareness is about such ties, which are deeper even than our much explored relationship with our mothers. Pre-scientific people knew and felt this; to be healthy we must learn again to be as intimately aware of trees and mountains and animals as we are of our human relations. Children know this naturally, the poet Wordsworth observed, "until shades of the prison house close in".

The above words convey a comforting awareness that whatever the damage done to us from our relationships with parents and others we can 're-tune' ourselves back to total harmony with the higher power of Nature, remembering that the ancient word for breath is spirit.

Any relationship with others depends upon our relationship with ourselves and our ability to accept and develop our own gifts, talents, skills and creativity. We either respond to others through love, or fear. It is sobering to realise how much of our creativity is lost by the time we reach adulthood.

LOSS OF OUR RELATIONSHIP WITH
OUR CREATIVITY

Creativity in terms of an educational pyschologist research study as reported in *The Sunday Times* in the early 1960s. This report clearly highlights the loss of creativity in our children and young people as they make their way through early life and the education system.

Creativity at Birth   100%
Creativity measured on reaching School at Age 5   25%
Creativity measured on leaving Higher Education 2% in general
(School and University)   5% the very occasional exception

Relationships

LECTURE EXTRACT FROM
THE GREAT BIG TRUST'S LEVEL 7 COURSE
'INTRODUCTION TO CORRECT BREATHING'

Most of today's lecture is about relationships, and it may be challenging to suggest that if our relationship with ourselves is good, then our relationships with other people are generally good too, and visa versa. The factors that can upset relationships, are negative emotions and mindsets containing such negative energies as fear, hate, jealousy, greed, competitiveness, violence, addictions, and any others you can think of.

Our first thoughts about relationships may be the ones we have with a lover, partner, husband or wife, child, siblings or parents, but when we think about it, we realise that in some way we have a relationship with everyone we know, including ourselves. Since we are interested in public figures of all kinds, in that we either like them, or don't like them, we even have some kind of relationship with such people. We are sometimes influenced by those we may never meet within our 'culture of celebrities'.

Then, of course we have a relationship with our pets, cars, clothes and possessions. We think about them in a special way, and often have a sentimental feeling about our objects and possessions which may be beautiful or rare, and perhaps belonged to someone we loved. We also have a relationship with our home.

Think about the relationship we have with ourselves, which affects everything else we relate to. Having a relationship with anything involves thinking about them or it. All thoughts are energy, as we shall discuss more fully in another lecture. Energy is either positive or negative. All our energy goes out into the atmosphere, and by the law of magnetic attraction returns back to us in a positive or negative form, depending on how it was sent out.

As we correct our breathing, we begin to find subtle changes in our relationships. As we change, so do our relationships. Remember the better we breathe, the better our relationships become, because we find ourselves calmer and more relaxed. On the other hand sometimes relationships we created when we were more fearful, may have to move out of our lives, since they are no longer appropriate. In losing our fear of someone else we no longer allow them to dominate us.

We shall examine the power of thought in greater detail in another lecture. As our breathing improves we may find ourselves on a temporary plateau, where we seem to be attracting better relationships into our lives, while at the same time trying to find a way, without unkindness, of releasing old relationships which are no longer relevant to us.

The reason we want to do this without unkindness is that we are becoming calmer and wish to sort out problems in our lives without stress. Sometimes as well as relationships which are no longer relevant in our lives, we find that our attitude towards material possessions is changing, and we want to dispose of clothes, books, household items, we may have clung to from false sentimentality and a false sense of security. There is a useful saying: "Don't weep for anything which cannot weep for you." Using this as a yardstick it's amazing how much we can clear out of our lives, which is really surplus to the new 'me'. Then again, as we think we are suffering as we dispose of the old and worn-out, remember the words "don't sweat the small stuff, it's all small stuff". It really is, you know.

This is because the 'big stuff' brings us back to our relationship with ourselves and life itself. Our relationship with ourselves goes back to our first encounter with life when we were first born. We shall go into this more fully in another lecture, but it is important for us to briefly consider what life really is. We talk about life being a problem, or are over influenced by another person moaning about life being awful, but we have to stop and think of what we are talking about, *which is really what has been happening to us in our lives*. The fact is that you cannot actually see life, we can only note what happens to us and other people during our lifetime. We can only see the *results* of life, but never *see* life itself, because life is an invisible energy which we use while we are alive.

It is a scientific fact that the earth's energy vibration is on a fixed loving frequency known as Alpha, which never changes, otherwise the earth could go out of orbit and affect the other planets in the planetary system.

One of the interesting things to emerge from the results of correct breathing, which helps us to relax and stay relaxed, is that the electrical frequency of the human brain then changes to Alpha, and we feel peaceful and loving. It also brings about a balance between the left and right hemispheres of the brain. In addition, when breathing correctly, we harmonise with the earth's magnetic field which is always at Alpha. We might go further and discuss whether the intelligence which created the Universe might be a constant loving energy also! Obviously this energy must be greater than that of man, so it is rather comforting to think that we have a constant loving energy all round us which never changes. Much of what we understand as man's contribution to global warming must be attributed to mankind having used the loving energy of life in an incorrect way, through using stressful high Beta energy vibration, instead of the slower Alpha energies.

When a child is born its brain pattern for the first eight years of life is tuned in to the slower loving frequencies of Alpha and Theta. It knows about correct breathing, it is *born* knowing it. If we think about our own relationship with ourselves, it therefore seems safe to stay breathing correctly, because the earth's great vibration of love is constantly around us, and after all when our brain is at Alpha, we feel peaceful and loving.

It is safe and right to love ourselves, otherwise how can we truly love anyone else? There are two great sayings: "It's OK not to be perfect." and "It's OK to make a mistake." There is no real excuse to criticise ourselves as we so love to do!

Sometimes when we behave in a less than perfect way, or make a mistake, we start to dislike ourselves. It is OK to note our failings, but always to keep loving ourselves, As the saying goes, "The highest intelligence made you, and it don't make trash!" So we mustn't trash what has been created by the highest energy.

Obviously we may not like some of our failings, nor those of others, in fact we may loathe them, but we have to remain loving.

This means that our relationship with ourselves must stay loving, and it is correct to surround ourselves with people who feel the same way as we do. It makes for joyful and spiritual relationships in which we have room to grow. In that context we have to look at our other relationships and perhaps question if they still have a place in our lives. As we realise that we are *growing* in many ways, we may recognise that some of our friends are not travelling on the same path with us, and we accept that we have no longer much in common.

We do not have to feel guilty in moving on, for we must not hold ourselves back. We are beginning to make new and more satisfying relationships. Old friends may still remain so, but will become less important in our lives, because they have not gone through the open door we see for us, and want to go through.

We cannot take them, and it would be wrong to try to. We must all have freewill in this matter of change, which is why we must never advise someone unasked that we could help them with their faulty breathing, or tell someone that they are breathing incorrectly. We cannot allow our ego to impose or interfere with someone else's freedom of choice, or make the judgement that they are not perfect. If they ask us to help or show them, that is a different matter. We are all here because we are interested in correct breathing, and it is important to talk about the changes that may happen in our lives, which as a result will always be for the better.

You may have heard about a process called Transactional Analysis. It reminds us that there are three kinds of relationships, that of a parent, a child and an adult. We assume that as we grow up we leave our child behind, and no longer need a parent, but in many cases that does not happen. We may be of adult age, but we find that we have a relationship with a partner or friend, who treats us in a parental way, telling us what we should or should not do, and as a result we feel like a helpless child. We may have a little bit of an unfinished child within us, and may go on for a long time accepting that domination, feeling guilty if we feel rebellious, but try to hide our resentment. On the other hand, we ourselves may have a relationship with someone who is an adult, and yet we always seem to be looking after them, feeling guilty if we leave them to sort out their own problems.

In neither of the two cases quoted above are the two adults behaving in a mature way, both have personal growth to complete. Many of us are in situations of this kind, and as we improve our breathing, we often realise that we have to move away from such relationships. This is a good sign and necessary for our development and growth, but we may go through a difficult period, as we try to do so, without appearing to be unkind.

As mature adults we will never tolerate domination in our lives from a parental or childish person, because it prevents us from being true to ourselves, and following our right path. In his wise little book, *Heal Thyself*, Dr. Edward Bach suggests, for our own development, the importance of freeing ourselves from people who control us, as well as healing our own urge to control people, and likens the process to a game of sport. Try to love the person if possible, but treat the process of disengaging as if we were 'playing a game of sport', but never allowing 'the least bit of interference'. Everyone has their own survival kit within them, and we all have to find and use this 'do it yourself' information eventually if we are to mature.

Most of us feel uncomfortable when we hate another person, in fact hard and challenging as it may seem there is a deep moral law within each of us which knows that we must love everyone. It can help if we accept that we do not have to like them, or what they do! If we don't love other people, the lack of love has to be in our thoughts, which prevents us from loving ourselves. Why let someone else spoil our relationship with ourselves? It means we are in their control. No way!

There is another threat if we can call it that, which is when two people who have rather drifted along perhaps for many years, seem to be drifting apart. One of the couple. may have begun to explore alternative disciplines and has begun to grow and change. They suddenly realise that this is not possible within the existing relationship and begin to feel suffocated within its confines, as if they were in a cage. Sooner or later they have to get out of the cage, difficult as it may be. In any relationship which is healthy, one and one is more than two. In an unhealthy relationship, one and one is less than two. We have to face that truth, if we are to be true to ourselves, and that is number one priority. We cannot take the other person through the door which we know is waiting for us to open. We all have to sort this process out for ourselves. It may be comforting to understand that if the other person does not now know the 'real you', what value is there in such a relationship? We may in fact be preventing them from finding someone with whom they are more compatible.

Many people are frightened to free themselves from a parental or childish partnership, because they are frightened of being alone. It is indeed a challenge, but more rewarding than to remain in that claustrophobic union. It is a wonderful discovery to become friends with yourself, and to realise as that wise lady, Lilla Bek expressed, "It is only when we are on our own that our unseen guides and helpers can speak to us, so that the silence is pregnant with possibility."

Then we have our relationships with pets and possessions. It is of course great to love an animal, and when a pet passes on, our loss may be more acute than losing a loved person. Of course it is right and proper to grieve, but when the person is still in unremitting grief after many years, it is as if someone is in a time-warp from which they do not want to emerge. Perhaps they did not become mature before embarking on a dependency relationship, and feel they have no identity without it.

Loneliness can seem a frightening experience. It takes time to become friends with oneself, which is what we are all meant to do.

THEN TO BE ALONE CAN BE AN ADVENTURE.

As mentioned earlier we learn that the vibrational frequency of the earth's magnetic field is always at Alpha, a loving force-field in which we exist and from which we draw our breath.

Sometimes people may feel that if they had a bad and abusive childhood, they are doomed to be unhappy for life. Not to have had loving parents is of course a great sorrow. Yet in his book *The Voice of the Earth*, Theodore Roszak points out that our deepest link is with Nature, which is deeper than our relationship with our parents. It may take some time before we allow ourselves to trust this truth, but when we accept that the life-force of the Earth vibrates constantly on a loving beat, then we can begin to heal ourselves. The term Mother Earth does mean just that, and it is wonderfully satisfying to experience this closeness, as of a loving parent.

Christmas nativity calendars are an interesting teaching aid to demonstrate the relationship between parents and children, the kind with little doors and chocolates inside each door, bought quite cheaply from a supermarket. Each has 25 'windows' usually concealing a little chocolate, which we can refer to as the gifts brought into the world at birth by a child. Each window in the child's calendar when opened, represents the gift of love, courage, humour, joy, patience, creativity, forgiveness, communication, compassion, etc., you can think of any others you may wish to add to complete the 25.

If you refer to what we will call the parent's calendar, a number of these windows will be closed by the time we reach adulthood or are able to bring a child into the world. If *our* gifts of the spirit contained within the windows of the adult's calendar have been closed down, how can we expect those of the child to remain open? The first eight years are critical. Through its work on correct breathing the Great Big Trust has proved time and again that we can re-open our closed windows using the activity of correct breathing. It is never too late.

In mature relationships we do not seek approval as from a parent, we know within ourselves what to do. If we are true to ourselves we cannot hurt anyone else, and all changes will be for the good of everyone concerned, whether or not they may realise it at the time.

So much change can happen in our lives as we become true to correct breathing, that it is appropriate to reflect, and decide what good mature relationships are really about.

If you study any of the quoted testimonials and extracts in this book, taken to their basic meaning, they all come down to our relationship with ourselves. *It is now always safe to be kind, loving and gentle with myself.*

* * *

Testimonials from people who have benefited through using Correct Breathing

Correct Breathing has given me:

1. Poise
2. Total control in the classroom
3. Reduced fear and anxiety (virtually to nil)
4. Enormous reserves of energy
5. Alertness
6. The ability to think
7. Ability to Irish dance (took to it like a duck to water)
8. God

Mary, senior teacher of biology

Well I find that I can relax now, where I never ever could before and have learned to sit on a chair and breathe properly. I can sit for a few minutes, put my feet flat on the floor and feel a lot better. I did it waiting in the Doctor's surgery the other morning and it works.

I also find that I do it a couple of times a day, and always at night in bed. I find that then I fall asleep. I think that it has been really good, as I never, ever, could relax and I am learning now. I don't say that I am really good at it, but I am certainly learning to do it, and I do feel better for it.

Katrina

There is more than one thing wrong with me, indeed there are two or three things that I have been seeing to. I have been to hospital a few times, but now that I am using the Correct Breathing I feel much better.

Joan

* * *

Excerpts from Student Essays

GREAT BIG TRUST, LEVEL 7 INTRODUCTION
TO CORRECT BREATHING COURSE

The child born into a negative environment becomes locked into the fight or flight response. Living life in fear, beginning its life in a busy delivery room where the nursing staff and doctors are over worked, over tired and too harassed to help calm and relax the stressed mother. The baby surrounded by noise and activity, the stress of the situation transferring to the baby, going home to possibly, a broken or dysfunctional family, themselves incorrect breathers, stressed by poor living conditions, overcrowding, poverty and domestic abuse. The stressed parents, taking their problems out on the innocent child, the child witnessing negative behaviour, believing themselves to be the cause. Surrounded by smokers, alcohol or substance misuse, all contributing to the poor atmosphere and oxygen levels. A child born into such an environment/lifestyle can become stifled, in growth, development and spirit.

June

Eastern philosophies such as yoga and Buddhism are aware of energy pathways throughout and surrounding the body. The correct breath energy pathways rise up from the solar plexus (in the abdomen between the navel and the pelvic bone) to the opening of the 'crown chakra' which represents a higher or spiritual consciousness. We begin to see that we are unique in our own set of blueprints that determine not only who we are, but that we also have a contribution to the world we live in. A set of truths that we want to live by that are loving and are given to us intuitively from this unseen source.

Karen

* * *

Realise that when we learn to breathe efficiently, the natural process of meditation flows freely, and manifests as an integral part of one's being; understand that meditation without form is simply the observation and ending of the conscious processes of the noise inside your head without using effort. Which means you must go into it yourself. Uplift your body, mind and spirit.

The mind is constantly talking incessantly, even when the mouth is closed. There is a way in which you can turn that off, many of your problems in this life stem from all that noise going on inside you. Once you feel the power of meditation you will find it very interesting and a great delight. Fulfill your greatest dreams through meditation, and discover the art of knowing and loving yourself.

Linda

What other Visionary Writers have said about Breathing and Life

And I sometimes wonder if the reluctance of conventional medicine to examine my own ideas on even the lowest level, and to try my method when there is no other method to try, cannot be summed-up by a simple exchange of words.

This took place between a student whom I had aided back to normal life and an eminent surgeon who had earlier confessed himself powerless to help and who (although now impressed by the results of my treatment) feared for his reputation if he recommended it to his own patients.

"I suppose" – my student said – "that it's better to die officially than to be cured unofficially."

The surgeon smiled with some regret. "Yes," he said, "I'm afraid that's about true."

William P. Knowles, New Life Through Breathing

* * *

We must earnestly learn to develop individuality according to the dictates of our own Soul, to fear no man and to see that no-one interferes with, or dissuades us from, the development of our evolution, the fulfilment of our duty and the rendering of help to our fellow men, remember that the further we advance, the greater blessing we become to those around.

Dr. Edward Bach, Heal Thyself

The main reason for the failure of modern medical science is that it is dealing with results and not causes. For many centuries the real nature of disease has been masked by materialism, and thus disease itself has been given every opportunity of extending its ravages, since it has not been attacked at its origin. The situation is like to an enemy strongly fortified in the hills, continually waging guerilla warfare in the country around, while the people, ignoring the fortified garrison, content themselves with repairing the damaged houses and burying the dead, which are the results of the raids of the marauders. So generally speaking, is the situation in medicine to-day; nothing more than patching up of some attacked and burying of those who are slain, without a thought being given to the real stronghold.

Disease will never be cured or eradicated by present materialistic methods, for the simple reason that disease in its origin is not material. What we know as disease is an ultimate result produced in the body, the end product of deep and long acting forces, and even if material treatment alone is apparently successful this is nothing more than a temporary relief unless the real cause has been removed.

Dr. Edward Bach, Heal Thyself

Any individual, whether adult or child, part of whose work it is in this life to free himself from the dominant control of another, should remember the following: firstly, that his would-be oppressor should be regarded in the same way as we look upon an opponent in sport, as a personality with whom we are playing the game of Life, without the least trace of bitterness, and that if it were not for such opponents we should be lacking the opportunity of developing our courage and individuality; secondly, that the real victories of life come through love and gentleness, and that in such a contest no force whatever must be used: that by steadily growing in his own nature, bearing sympathy, kindness and, if possible, affection - or, even better, love - towards the opponent, he may so develop that in time he may very gently and quietly follow the call of conscience without allowing the least interference.

Dr. Edward Bach, Heal Thyself

In all things cheerfulness should be encouraged, and we should refuse to be oppressed by doubt and depression, but remember that such are not of ourselves, for our Souls know only joy and happiness.

Dr. Edward Bach, Heal Thyself

This above all: to thine own self be true,
And it must follow, as the night the day,
Thou canst not then be false to any man.

Shakespeare, Hamlet

We want to love people but usually only in the condition we want them to be. If we're not awake to the one thing that we share in common, which is air, then how can we love each other unconditionally?

Reshad Feild, Breathing Alive

Breath also contains moisture. Every little droplet of moisture on the breath can contain loving thoughts; or it can contain negativity, producing with it an atmosphere which is surely not going to give pleasure and joy to the world. The moisture can collect floating thought forms in the same way that we can get hay fever from the pollen of grasses and flowers that we are allergic to. We need to get our water system organised - i.e. that 80 per cent of us which is mainly a thought-collector. With conscious use of the breath we can combine the elements of fire, earth, air and water into an alchemical marriage to distil the thought-forms that are no longer necessary in the world.

Reshad Feild, Breathing Alive

The greatest healing in the world is being yourself

Reshad Feild, Breathing Alive

To be normal is indeed a very great challenge. Imagine what a breath of relief it will be when we actually know we are normal. We are balanced. Our in-breath and our out-breath are balanced. We love as we know we are loved. The womb of the moment, lying within the pause between the two breaths of life and death, is a world of infinite possibility, waiting to give birth to a new cycle of Mankind - the Golden Age that we have heard about for so long.

Reshad Feild, Breathing Alive

Affirmations

AN AFFIRMATION IS A POSITIVE STATEMENT OF ABSOLUTE TRUTH. REPEAT IT TO YOURSELF OR WRITE IT OUT TO RE-AFFIRM SOMETHING THAT YOU WANT TO BECOME TRUE.

There is enough for everyone, including me.

I now deserve to be prosperous, all the time.

I am now ready to accept prosperity into my life, in whatever form it manifests.

It is OK for me to have what I want.

I am complete, whole and satisfied, right now. I am loved just for being myself.

I now express my love and creativity in my work

It's now safe for me to feel all my feelings.

Life is easy.

It's safe for me to let go and relax.

Love is my natural state of being.

My endless good now comes to me in endless ways.

My happiness is built upon a rock. It is mine now and for all eternity.

Inspirational quotes to help on your Breathing Journey

To love and be loved is the greatest happiness

Sidney Smith

Come out of the circle of time, and into the circle of love

Rumi

The heart has its reasons that the mind knows nothing of.

Blaise Pascal

The best portion of a good man's life - his little nameless, unremembered acts of kindness and of love.

William Wordsworth

The goody-goodies are the thieves of virtue

Confucius

* * *

PART EIGHT

The Power of Thought and Spirituality

AFTER WE BEGIN TO IMPROVE our breathing we start to notice changes in the way we think, and realise that many thoughts that we have previously taken for granted for years and years are no longer relevant or correct. We have not received counselling, become involved in one of many traditional or alternative therapies, some of which cost hundreds of pounds. Yet we know that this 'new' thinking is authentic, and we begin to take action arising from these thoughts. We have free-will to continue to breathe correctly, or drop back into the old ways. However the new thinking is beginning to reveal to us that many of our relationships are shallow, and based on domination or being dominated, which is no longer acceptable. We have begun to feel more confident and see broader horizons for our lives, which we know are achievable and which we have to bring into being for our own personal development and for the good of all. Where before we may have been apt to tell white lies etc., a new morality seems to be emerging into our consciousness which could be described as *spiritual*, without becoming involved in any organised religious dogma. All these changes are connected with our relationship to ourselves, which of course affects our relationships with others. We realise that we cannot turn our backs on such positive changes even although we may do so for a time. Eventually we realise that there is a 'safety' in this new way of living, which is not dependent upon scientific discoveries, but from a higher consciousness within ourselves which becomes daily more precious, even sacred.

We discover with joy often through inexplicable coincidences, that other people have trodden this same path of personal regeneration, and are prepared to be alone without feeling lonely. Often the lives and writings of those who have gained self-mastery become our new companions. We gradually make new friends with people who are currently treading this same path, without becoming dismissive of other people. We also learn a new humility which appreciates that everyone contains a valuable spiritual truth. These changes or growth in our relationships are not necessarily over-serious, indeed may provoke much laughter and hilarity. We realise that everyone is on their own path of discovery, and we have to release expectations from other people of how we or they should be, in a growing awareness that all we have to do is live each day to the full according to our own inner voice of truth.

The Power of Thought and Spirituality

LECTURE EXTRACT FROM
THE GREAT BIG TRUST'S LEVEL 7 COURSE
'INTRODUCTION TO CORRECT BREATHING'

To heal our breathing means co-operating with the basic rules of nature. To breathe incorrectly means to disobey these rules, which so often eventually leads to unhappy and unfulfilled lives.

As our breathing begins to improve we realise that something is happening inside our head and hearts! Everything is the same, only different. The reason is that a better oxygen supply is opening up information stored in brain cells, which may have been dormant for many years. We may have felt that something has been missing in our lives, but are not sure what it is. Now we begin to know.

One of the major changes is that you will have more energy. By contrast you may temporarily experience extreme fatigue for a period, your body is telling you that you have not been giving it enough rest, and are overdrawn on your energy bank. Respect this fatigue, and give yourself more rest, it is essential to top up your energy batteries, so that the better energy inspired, by better breathing can be used creatively.

The other important change you will notice will be in your thoughts. You may realise that it is time to change some old thought habits, remember all action and change come from our thoughts. Each thought we have uses energy.

It is said that we have about 80,000 thoughts a day, and really there are only two kinds of thought, positive or negative, the source of which are either love or fear. Poor breathing and resultant negative thinking is often linked to deeply buried fear, the source of which we have forgotten, but is still exerting its presence unconsciously in our psyche.

As people begin to improve their breathing, they realise that they can no longer accept situations and people who have been controlling their lives. They find the courage to make changes, to say "no", where before they would have agreed for the sake of peace, even if their intuition told them that it was wrong to do so. They are now beginning to regain confidence, lose some of their fears, and starting to listen to their intuition. These three qualities are the main ingredients in regaining control of our lives, but our thoughts have to change before we can take the necessary action.

As our breathing improves, our brain cells start to 'twinkle'. More and more new creative thoughts start to flow into our minds, often quite contrary to those we have held before about people, places and things.

If we start to think about our estimated 80,000 thoughts a day, some negative, some positive, we need to realise that there are 80,000 x 80,000 possibilities, from one positive and 79,999 negative, to one negative and 79,999 positive. Most of us will have perhaps a fifty-fifty split or countless variations in between. Where do our thoughts come from, and why are some people very positive, and others pessimistic? Those who see the cup as half-full or half-empty? Obviously we have established our own individual mind-set, and we usually need to go back to our childhood or even birth to investigate our thought origins.

You will probably agree that a positive thought will attract a positive return, and a negative thought the opposite, since thought is an energy and the magnetic attraction of our thoughts bounces back to us.

Can you see a thought? The answer is "no". Can you see life? The answer is also "no". You may disagree, but we can only see the *results* of anything which is using the energy of life, not the energy of life itself, even although we know that energy is being used.

The next question is when did you have your first thought about life? Many people will think of this as our first *memory*, but the truth is that we had our first thought as we were born, as we entered life, as a baby and separate individual from our mother. It is amazing how we fail to accept that a baby can have a thought, even although it can cry when it is hungry, so it must know that it needs fed. So many babies are born by Caesarian section, premature, breech, forceps, induction or have the umbilical cord cut too soon. The mother and the birth attendants may be very stressful. The room may be too hot, too cold, too noisy. It is very possible that our first thought about life was a very negative one.

Our first thoughts about life are the most important we shall ever have, they are the foundation of our thought pattern. A little baby comes into life from a quiet place, its brain rhythm is close to Nature, yet its first experience of life may be so negative that it will think that it has failed at the most important challenge it will ever face. Why is that so? What did we do at our birth? We left the safe place, couldn't change our mind, came along a tunnel where we had never been before, had to put all our efforts and a bit more to find the way out, **but we did not have to ask anyone's permission, or try to please anyone.** Did you make it? Of course, congratulations! You have already succeeded in the most difficult and dangerous undertaking of your lives, except that because of all the difficulties you seemed to meet (already referred to), you may have thought that you had made a mistake. You did not, you were victorious despite the problems, so give yourself credit. Everyone did their best, maybe a poor best, perhaps limited by current ideas and trends, to try to help you into life.

Can you find out what was your most negative thought about life, which you may have created at your birth, and which has been sabotaging you ever since? **Yes. You can.**

Think about the three things which you would most like to have in your life? After much discussion we all really want the same things in a way that is personal to *us*. These are perfect loving relationships with many people, including perhaps a loving partner, the perfect work which develops and uses our deepest talents and skills, and the perfect home in the right place. Remember we are all unique, so what is right for us individually will not be right for someone else. Also these wishes are loving, and life is also loving, as we learn in another lecture, i.e. the rhythm of the Earth is at Alpha a loving vibration, so what we most wish for our lives is *already here*, even although we may not yet have it or only part of it at this moment.

Perhaps a few people may suggest what the thought is they hold, or have some idea about the thought that prevents them having what they most want. We may consider, if not prove, that this thought is negative and it may have been the first one at their birth. Such a powerful but **incorrect** thought about life was incorrect, because at our birth we got what we most wanted, which was LIFE, and we will never want anything more. We got what we most wanted despite all the odds!

As we improve our breathing and more positive thoughts begin to arise, they may seem to be at war with long-held negative thoughts, which is why it may be important to spend some time on the Power of our Thoughts. Some birth thoughts may be "It is too difficult to get what I most want." "Everyone stops me getting what I most want." "I'm not good enough to get what I most want." No-one stopped you, they did their best, and remember if you had been too afraid you would not have made it.

If you can think about what is your most negative thought about life, it is now safe to change it, even a little at a time i.e. "I don't believe I can have what I most want." to "sometimes I can have what I most want." "A little more often I can have what I most want." "Quite often I can have what I most want." "A lot of the time", "most of the time", "ALL THE TIME". What you want is loving, and it suits everyone for you to have it, because you are not taking what belongs to them. You are taking what is yours and is on your vibration. They are on a different vibration to yours, one which is personally unique to them. **Change your thoughts, change your life. It is now safe for you to have what you most want.**

Changes in the way we think often introduce a dimension into our lives, which may seem new, and which we cannot always share with our friends until we can sort it out, and have a name for it.

Albert Einstein was not only a great scientist, but was also a profound thinker. He said:

> Matter including the body consists of a field of energy organised in a unique way. There is evidence that some of this energy exists in another dimension which I shall call the fourth part of the body. And it is by virtue of this fourth part of a human that communication with the Universal Intelligence is made possible. If it is likely that this phenomenon we are trying to understand exists in a dimension without energy, science as we know it will never be able to measure it, and I feel it is futile and wasteful to try and validate any of these phenomena to the traditional scientific community.

We are led to believe that unless something has been validated by scientific thought and theory, or provable by scientific formula then it is questionable. It is cheering to have a statement from someone who was one of the world's most eminent scientists, that science will never have all the answers!

When we breathe correctly and sometimes enter a deep meditative state, we often emerge feeling that we have been in touch with a Higher Consciousness which has communicated to our own consciousness. This connection has great meaning for us, and yet we may feel that other people will make fun of us if we express our feelings about it. On reflection these thoughts are what Einstein meant when he talked about the fourth dimension, and it is useful to have his words handy when you are speaking to a cynic who only recognises scientific facts. They probably will not have heard of Einstein's words on Higher Consciousness, and you can have harmless amusement in being surprised at their lack of awareness of the words of a Master. Still it is not really worth trying to convert a cynic, you know what you have discovered within yourself.

Another name for this Higher Consciousness is *spirituality*, again a word that not everyone is comfortable with, but which is increasingly mentioned surprisingly in more former, orthodox communications. You will increasingly understand its meaning as you correct your breath, because the word breath means *spirit* in some ancient languages. The ancients probably knew exactly what it was – Einstein's Higher Consciousness!

A recently discovered saying is **"If something isn't spiritual, it isn't."** The implication is that unless something is not energised by the truth it cannot leave an impact.

Within each of us lies what is referred to as the true self, or the joyful loving innocent child, which is our duty to protect within our adult maturity. A profound thinker called Bronson Alcott, father of Louise Alcott who wrote the well-known book *Little Women*, was a visionary educator, who believed that the new-born soul of a child "carried within it the imprint of spirit and wisdom". He wrote a book called *How Like an Angel came I Down*.

Perhaps this special part of ourselves we are encountering through our breath is the angelic child, which prevents us behaving in ways in which we are all tempted, carrying grudges, resentment, unforgiveness, not loving ourselves or others, If we add anger, greed, lust, jealousy, we are all inheritors of a box of 'nasties' which, because of our higher breath consciousness, are no longer acceptable. One by one we dislodge them from our psyche, because we realise that we are spiritually weakened through holding them in our consciousness. Take unforgiveness; if we hold that thought towards another, we are allowing them to control us, and why should we give them that control?

It is often within our own families that we have to start this pruning process, saying "I love you" to a parent who never said it to us. We do not like what they did, but if we do not love everyone, we lessen our love for ourselves. Thank goodness there is a difference between loving and liking!

There are a number of books about breathing and spirituality such as Reshad Feild's *Breathing Alive,* or *The Healing Power of Breath* by Jonathan Daemion, which take the understanding of breathing beyond the purely physical act which is essential for health. Breathing correctly is so much more than that, if we only live in the day to day rituals of eating, work, etc., we are only using about a seventh of what is our true reality. We cannot see it, we can only re-discover it, it is patterned in our cells, but needs the energy of life, through Correct Breathing, to release it. That energy is spirit-breath.

Life then becomes infinitely richer, everything we do has a deep meaning, everyone we meet is truly another spirit whatever their faults. We do not have to be perfect, we can make mistakes, and still be spiritual.

One of the interesting manifestations of correct breathing, is the extra significance we perceive in colour, often colour we see in our breathing practice. It will be one of the colours and shades of the spectrum, red, orange, yellow, green, blue, indigo, violet.

In Eastern philosophy the use of the energy of life is known as *prana*. We read about the chakras, invisible yet powerful centres of energy throughout the body. The seven centres lie between the base of the spine to the crown of the head, the lower being red and the upper violet, higher spiritual. Between these two points the other colours resonate, orange reproductive, yellow solar plexus, green the heart, blue the throat, indigo between the eyes (third eye), and the violet at the crown often represented as a lotus flower. To see these colours often very strongly as we breathe, often means that one of our chakras is opening up, we feel there is a deep significance and meaning to the phenomenon. We see life in a more enlightened way.

Eastern philosophies such as yoga and Buddhism have added a

real significance to our western understanding of the spiritual dimension, and our present culture would be poorer without their influence. By the same token we have brought our own spiritual insights to the East, even it has yet to recognise that fact! We cannot force spirituality on ourselves, all our changes must seem 'right', nor must we force ourselves to be like anyone else. We may admire great teachers who have gone before, but never underestimate your own unique contribution to the limitless layers of spiritual truths. You have a spiritual contribution to make which no other person has. Many truths come to us from the most unexpected people who we may have underestimated. Humility is a wonderful word when we think of spirituality, probably the most spiritual people are just that, humble but rich in the wisdom of the fourth dimension.

You are your own Devil, you are your on God, you fashioned the paths your footsteps have trod,
And no-one can save you from sorrow and sin Until you have lis't to the Spirit within.

Attributed to a Maori

Testimonials from people who have benefited through using Correct Breathing

I think there should be more therapists trained in the work on breathing, there is a need for education and training in this field for the future.

Psychotherapist, Research and Ethics

I will never again let everyday worries get me down.

Housewife

* * *

I felt a lot better in situations of stress. I feel calmer in situations regarding both work and at home after doing my breathing. I have felt physically different and handled situations differently. I asked my wife if she found any difference with me, and she took some time to come round and say "yes". There are no raised voices now in situations, and I am still calm with my daughter. I find that with the breathing work I have better control.

Robert, a high blood pressure sufferer

My communication has been stuck, but this has been better (with breathing) and I am being listened to now. My fear levels have reduced.

Margaret

Came full of stress from working conditions in the NHS. Feel working on my breathing pattern has brought changes to the fore for me to deal within in different areas of my life, i.e. parenthood, Spiritual growth, unfair treatment at work. Correct Breathing has helped me onto another rung of my growth ladder.

Marion

Thank you for the glimpse of my tomorrows. I am confident I will be breathing better now. Gained a better understanding of me.

Emma

Excerpts from Student Essays

GREAT BIG TRUST, LEVEL 7 INTRODUCTION TO CORRECT BREATHING COURSE

Correct breathing allows us to access higher levels of consciousness. Breathers often receive insight, clarity and spiritual gifts during and after sessions. With each breathing session the participant becomes lighter and clearer as they gain the ability to see past illusion and follow their own inner guidance. To practice the art of correct breathing is an exercise in personal transformation, it is safe and effective with results being experienced immediately. It heightens self awareness, delivers self healing and promotes self empowerment. It is for everyone.

Hugh

In conclusion we can say that chronic pain, mental suffering and disease are caused by a lack of oxygen in our bodies. The only way this life giving substance can get into our bodies is through our breath. It is therefore critically important that we are all made aware of this simple truth and start to recognise our breathing as one of the most important things in our life. We will then be able to liberate ourselves from the learned destructive behaviour of anger, fear, worry and jealousy. Only then will we be able to experience and express unconditional love which is the greatest healing force on the earth. Consequently we will rescue the earth from devouring itself through human created diseases such as hate and war. We may then create a better society, one bursting with positive relationships and loving communication.

Ewan

What other Visionary Writers have said about Breathing and Life

Breath is life, the basic and most fundamental expression of our life. In Judaism *ruah*, the breath, means the spirit of God that infuses the creation; in Christianity there is also a profound link between the Holy Spirit, without which nothing could have life, and the breath. In the teaching of Buddha, the breath, or prana in Sanskrit, is said to be the 'vehicle of the mind', because it is the prana that makes our mind move. So when you calm the mind by working skilfully with the breath, you are simultaneously and automatically taming and training the mind. Haven't we all experienced how relaxing it can be when life is stressful, to be alone for a few minutes and just breathe, in and out, deeply and quietly? Even such a simple exercise can help us a great deal.

Sogyal Rinpoche, Meditation

You are not your mind. You are a thinker of your thoughts.

Mary & Ray Brooks,
Spirit, Mind, Body The Technique of Affirmation

Negative thinking has become epidemic in our world. During the course of every day, each of us may be the source of hundreds of negative thoughts concerning impending disasters (large and small). We may also worry about negative outcomes; create images of being undeserving or unworthy of good things in life; hold on to ideas about being rejected, offended, or betrayed; and exaggerate notions of the importance of everyday aches and pains. Thought is a powerful creative force; thinking helps create the world in which we live.

Given that billions of people are out there creating those negative thoughts, it should be no wonder that we live in a world that is violent, polluted, unhappy, and in great need of healing.

Nathaniel Altman, The Oxygen Prescription

Learning to breathe properly and learning to use the power of our thoughts for our own benefit are the two most important activities a human can learn. Therefore, they deserve to be the focus of any educational system that is intended to be valuable or practical. Teaching Breath Awareness should be a most important theme in all schools.

Leonard Orr, Breath Awareness

* * *

The psychology of breathing holds the promise of becoming an important area of study within the new biological discipline of respiratory psychophysiology. Breathing may well be the bridge between psychology and physiology.

Beverly H. Timmons and Ronald Ley [Editors],
Behavioural and Psychological Approaches to Breathing Disorders

Breath is the rainbow bridge that unites body, mind and spirit. Seen physically, it is full and easy movement of air in the body. Seen mentally, it is loving intuition bringing harmony to chaos. Seen spiritually, it is the creative act that makes everything out of nothing.

Jim Morningstar, Breathing in Light and Love

Negative thoughts weigh heavily on the abdomen and disrupt its proper functioning. The body is isolated from the mind and the rupture between the two brains is total.

Pierre Pallardy,
Gut Instinct - What your stomach is trying to tell you

The best-kept traditions of how to use the full power of the breath are mainly from the Asian countries of China, India, Japan and Tibet. As a result, the breath has a very different role in these countries. Breathing is used for healing and maintaining good health, as well as for spiritual advancement.

Gunnel Minett, Exhale: An Overview of Breathwork

And there is also another aspect of the in-breath. If we are not awake, we may breathe in the results of our own negative emotions or thoughts and even share in those of others. We breathe in thoughts held in the moisture of the breath.

Reshad Feild, Breathing Alive

* * *

When we are mindful of our breathing, it helps us to calm the body and the mind. Then we are able to be aware of our thoughts and feelings with a greater degree of calmness and with a more discerning eye. We are able to see things more clearly and with a larger perspective... And with this awareness comes a feeling of having more room to move, of having more options, of being free to choose effective and appropriate responses. (Kabat-Zinn)

Jane Boston and Rena Cook [Editors], Breath in Action

The Divine, however we perceive it, is in every breath we take.

*Joy Manne, CONSCIOUS BREATHING -
How Shamanic Breathwork Can Transform Your Life*

Affirmations

AN AFFIRMATION IS A POSITIVE STATEMENT OF ABSOLUTE TRUTH. REPEAT IT TO YOURSELF OR WRITE IT OUT TO RE-AFFIRM SOMETHING THAT YOU WANT TO BECOME TRUE.

It is now safe for me to release the past.

I now forgive myself and my parents for all past errors

I now love and accept myself exactly as I am.

It is now safe for me to be close to people

I now love everyone and everyone loves me.

I am now at peace with myself and the whole world.

My endless good now comes to me in endless ways.

*My happiness is built upon a rock.
It is mine now and for all eternity.*

Inspirational quotes to help on your Breathing Journey

The true meaning of life is to plant trees,
under whose shade you do not expect to sit.

Nelson Henderson

For man is by nature an artist.

Tagore

Everywhere I go I find a poet has been there before me.

Sigmund Freud

Don't listen to what they say. Go see.

Chinese Proverb

While it is true that an inherently free and scrupulous
individual may be destroyed, such an individual can never
be enslaved or used as a blind tool.

Albert Einstein

* * *

PART NINE

On Vibration,
Human Electricity, Healing,
Lymphatic System and the Heart

WHEN A PERSON BEGINS to understand the profound personal changes which start to happen as they correct their breathing, it is often found that in the enthusiastic wish to share this information with others, an unexpected wall of cynicism, disbelief, even ostracism is encountered from those once thought of as closest friends. However, to discount such positive inner changes is to turn one's back on the true self, which becomes unthinkable. Personal progress, once started, has to move forward, otherwise there is loss of integrity. A number of truths emerge from these experiences a) there is no point in entering into argument with the 'non believer' or cynic, b) a growing interest in the effect of correct breathing becomes very exciting, as we start to notice improvements in all aspects of our lives.

Eventually books or articles are discovered which talk about the effect of correct breathing on the electrical activity in the brain. This can be scientifically measured, and words such as vibration, healing etc, have a new meaning as we understand that correct breathing directly effects this electrical vibration in the brain, with a consequent beneficial effect on circulation, clearance of toxins, increase in energy, general well-being, and pleasure at being alive. In addition the positive energy that develops affects other people through our own self-healing.

Again, because electricity is invisible, although its effect is measurable, it becomes obvious that there is a great gap between those who understand the power of correct breathing on the electrical systems of the body, and the majority who have yet to recognise and acknowledge the simplicity of breathing as being the most powerful force available to us.

We are really not all that far forward in understanding the 'spiritual humility' required by us all in looking inwards and taking time to understand that our own individual breathing pattern may be the cause of all our own problems and collectively those of the world.

The most beautiful result of breathing correctly is the way in which our hearts open to the power of love in its purest form, and yet it is the only power which is really going to heal the nations of the earth, because it indicates that the right creative, intuitive, feminine, emotional side of the collective right brain of mankind has been opened. It signifies the importance of the feminine influence within the mind of man and also the masculine influence within the mind of woman.

In some ways it is possible to see such changes already happening among groups and communities world-wide, and it is important not to underestimate the catalytic power of such changes.

The book *The Awakened Mind* by the pioneer Maxwell Cade is an excellent reference source because it clearly demonstrates the the link between the electrical vibration of the brain and its dramatic effect on our ability to relax. His pioneering research work contributed towards the development of the Science of Bio-feedback towards the end of the 20th century. Various electrical recording and computerised devices, some small, some large, allowed people to note change in brain electrical activity and resultant changes in thought. The scarcity of public information about the electrical energy of the brain, and the powerful positive effect of correct breathing on brain balance, is almost a criminal deficit in the educational world, and the right which all children and students have to understand and apply these facts in their lives. The continuing emphasis on intellectual and left brain achievement can cause one to despair at the stupidity of the present lack of awareness amongst leaders and policy makers in the educational field.

Nevertheless the saying that 'there is no army strong enough to withstand an idea whose time has come', must surely hold true when applied to the dramatic life-enhancing results of Correct Breathing, and its power to rebalance the human system.

The knowledge that there is a proven basis of measured accuracy that one is not alone, or incorrect, in pursuing personal growth through correct breathing and relaxation, can be a source of relief to those undergoing a period of personal change. They accept that it is unnecessary to keep on feeling the need to prove the point, and find satisfaction in avoiding the waste of energy required to do so. A new language may arise, based on the understanding of the phrase 'wise as the serpent and gentle as the dove', enabling them to proceed on their personal journey without allowing the least interference, knowing that those who oppose their changes will certainly not be breathing correctly and are annoyed that they no longer have a dominating controlling influence over them.

There is no harm in repeating the succinct words of Enid Smithett, "We don't have to live our lives through other people's megalomania and we don't have to ask permission."

Vibration, Human Electricity, Healing, Lymphatic System and the Heart

LECTURE EXTRACT FROM
THE GREAT BIG TRUST'S LEVEL 7 COURSE
'INTRODUCTION TO CORRECT BREATHING'

This lecture is about several aspects of energy, and the way in which negative energy can affect our health.

Perhaps it is important to begin with the **lymphatic system** and its function. Because this course is not a medical one, it is not necessary to know about the lymphatic system apart from its basic purpose. It has a circulatory function in that it collects and transports waste tissue fluid through a series of filters back to the blood stream. [*continues on page 152*

Relationship of Correct Breathing to Physical, Mental and Emotional Health

(See diagrams on opposite page)

FIGURE 1: Electrical activity in healthy breathing shows a predominance of electrical activity in the lower diaphragm with relatively little in the upper chest.

This person will be calm, relaxed, not easily upset, and above all, healthy physically, mentally and emotionally.

FIGURE 2: As stress begins to rise the electrical activity increases in the upper chest and decreases in the lower diaphragm.

Consistent maintenance of this breathing pattern begins to produce classic symptoms of the early stages of stress - i.e. muscle tension, impaired circulation, fatigue, worry, headaches, fear, floating anxiety, and decreasing confidence.

This interference of the correct breathing pattern in young people **is at the root cause of addiction problems.**

FIGURE 3: High levels of electrical activity in the upper chest with little in the lower diaphragm is accompannied by stressful breathing and physical, mental and emotional symptoms.

This eventually leads to breakdown in body, mind, and emotions, if (a) the stress is not reduced by tackling and removing the cause(s), or (b) there is no education in correct breathe re-training to reduce stress should the cause(s) of the stress remain.

Unrelieved, the high electrical activity in the upper chest results in panic, phobias, and physical symptoms associated with serious and killer diseases and illness, including heart disease, cancer, ulcers etc. and acute addiction syndrome.

* * *

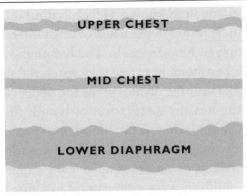

Fig 1: Healthy Breathing Pattern

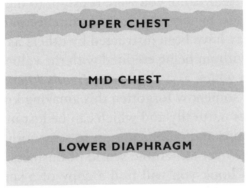

Fig 2: Initial Disturbance of Healthy Breathing Pattern

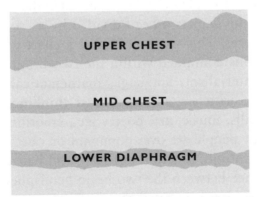

Fig 3: Acute Disturbance of Healthy Breathing Pattern,
leading to panic, phobias and mental & emotional breakdown.

This excess tissue fluid known as lymph fluid is colourless. Lymphatic vessels can be found in the walls of most internal organs, being similar in structure to blood vessels. The lymphatic vessels found in tissues are small, becoming larger as they reach the thoracic duct and right lymphatic duct near the thymus at the top upper centre of the chest.

Obviously the healthy circulation of lymph fluid is dependent upon the healthy circulation of the blood, and problems arise when the flow becomes sluggish and obstructions are formed.

The Brain. Many of us grew up with a suggestion from our educators, that children were either brainy or not brainy. Did you belong to the second category? Never fear, you have probably chosen this course because you were resistant to digesting facts and figures told to you by teachers, from an intellectual perspective. In the past you may have been instructed by others as to what a child *should* know, without being credited with the value of the wonderful information which as a child you **already knew**. Unfortunately our culture has somehow forgotten this amazing knowledge which a child possesses naturally and which can be lost in the pressure of curriculum, exams and qualifications, as yet another generation is prepared for the over-structured world of business and commerce.

Within this book you will find a copy of a small educational booklet containing a picture painted by a 16-year old schoolgirl, Janice Armstrong from Hawick High School in the Scottish Borders. In the picture she depicts a head divided by a cross into the two brain hemispheres. This section also has a chart which shows the various functions contained within the two brain areas; the left, objectivity, materialism, language, mathematical and scientific thought, logic, criticism and analytical thinking. On the right the creative skills, music, art, poetry etc., emotion-love, fear and intuition. Many people are over-dominant on one side, usually the left side. We can only function healthily and harmoniously when there is a balance between the two brain hemispheres. The World Health Organisation has stated that in Western civilisations 60% of people are dominated by the left brain hemisphere. The probable reason for our cultural sickness? Bureaucracy explained, endless forms? Where there is an imbalance there will always be a faulty breathing pattern, because we are out of harmony with nature, which is always balanced or moving towards balance.

With such an imbalance there is always a lack of connection between the second lower emotional brain and the upper intellectual brain, which you will learn about in this course. Tension will be observed across the diaphragm and solar plexus, as if the person was 'cut in half' by respiratory limitation. Restoring correct breathing, restores the balanced connection between the two brains, and the individual will again appear and feel calm and loving.

KORNERED

I'm addicted to FORMS
I fill them in swarms,
At handing them in, I am prime,
They say what I do do
       or will do or shall do
Statistic'ly all of the time.

This addiction to forms
For equating the 'norms'
Is leading me fast into crime
I now mark what I could do
       or would do or should do
For actual WORK I've no time.

Though my conscience is smitten
Of this I'm quite sure -
For this 'bug' once you're bitten
There isn't a cure.
Though the obvious answer
Too simple of course,
Is, to go to the fount head
AND BURN THEM AT SOURCE.

Poem by Janet Wilkins

True 'braininess' only occurs when the left and right hemispheres of the upper brain are balanced, with the intellectual head and emotional gut brains, and the heart which is placed between them, all working together. Recent discoveries show that the heart contains more brain cells than the brain, and in Eastern terms, is the last chakra to open. Could this be because the heart joins and amplifies the expression of the upper and lower brains through its loving alpha rhythms? Complete breathing from the bottom larger area of the lungs to the upper lobes, helps to restore brain balance, opening the heart in the process.

> The heart of a fool is in his mouth, the mouth of a wise man is in his heart.
>
> *Benjamin Franklin*

> The human heart feels things the eyes cannot see, and knows what the mind cannot understand.
>
> *Robert Valett*
> *(The heart feels, emotes and expresses)*

It might be worth discussing if in view of the World Health Statistics, whether 60% of Western countries are 'unbalanced'. Certainly out of balance with Nature, and likely to create systems also out of balance with Nature.

> **The vibration of mental forces are the finest and smallest, and consequently the most concentrated, potent and powerful in existence**
>
> *Charles Haanel*

There are a number of interesting subjects relating to the human mind and body, which are governed by the law of **vibration**. In other words everything that is alive has a vibration. This vibrational energy cannot be seen, but you have to imagine that this is happening in all living cells, and in every living organism.

Obviously there must be a natural law which defines the speed at which this vibration is taking place. It is said that even the wooden legs of a chair are vibrating at such a speed that it is the speed which holds the shape together. This is quite a difficult concept to grasp, and no doubt only observable through sophisticated scientific equipment.

We need to be constantly reminded that this law of vibration affects the human brain and subsequently the body, and the frequency of the electrical impulse, which is generated by our breathing. Everything is linked, because the brain impulse which governs the brain is activated by the way we think. All our cells are governed by this electrical frequency. The better we breathe, the more brain cells we activate, all twinkling away, hopefully at the right frequency depending on how correctly we breathe.

> We all know people who seem to vibrate with life, and others who seem dull and static. See how they breathe.
>
> *The Great Big Trust*

> I don't care what city you are living in, you've got enough power in your body to illuminate the whole city for nearly a week!
>
> *Bob Proctor*

> To become conscious of this wire is to become a live wire. The Universe is the live wire. It carries power to meet every situation in the life of every individual. When the individual mind touches the Universal mind, it receives all its power
>
> *Charles Haanel*

Healing. Many people these days are interested in the subject of healing, that is 'natural healing'. Healing really means to make better. If someone says that they are a healer, be a little wary, because true healers very rarely advertise themselves as such. There are many forms of healing, just as there are many forms of human disorders, from feeling out of sorts, to severe injury and disease.

In helping to heal someone, you need to stay detached, breathe correctly and be aware of being linked with Higher Consciousness, which is always on a loving vibration. If another person's vibrational electrical field is very weak, and you are not 'grounded', you may find yourself depleted, because you have given your energy away, instead of being a 'channel' for the endless energy of Higher Consciousness. All good healing energy is spiritual. Children are natural healers, they sense when we are out of balance, but they should not have to heal *us* all the same. If you are tense, just to sit next to someone who breathes correctly can help to heal you.

A wonderful old Doctor, Arthur Rowbotham, who trained at the Vienna school with Jung and Freud, was knocked down by a bus in his late seventies, and broke almost every bone in his body. He attributed his recovery to his ability to send healing energy to these places through his knowledge of breathing. Correct breathing helps the natural healing ability within the body to enable repair. Obviously breathing correctly keeps the circulation and lymphatic drainage flowing freely, to assist regeneration of the cells.

Spiritual healing, which restores the sense of self identity, plays an important part in the restoration of harmony when someone is suffering from nervous illness. The human nervous system is like a finely tuned instrument, and needs to be restored to its natural vibration, for healing to take place.

We have perhaps attached too much of a mystery label to the art of healing, as if healing was only able to take place under the NHS, but that organisation does not claim to be spiritual, or acknowledge the place of breath as the most powerful healer. A former retiring president of the Royal College of Physicians said "they (doctors) should pay more attention to the spiritual dimension".

The restoration of correct breathing sometimes restores to us the gift of seeing colour around another human being. Again another faculty probably taken for granted in ancient times. This is of course known as the aura, and appears as a single or many coloured band of colour around another person. It is probably always there, although most people do not see it. No doubt we all could do with a little training. Some people can tell if a person is healthy by seeing the colour of their aura, a good clear blue, green, pink or lavender is beautiful to see, but there are muddy yellows and browns which signify a lack of vitality, and possibly bad health.

The study of energy is endlessly fascinating, because nothing can happen without a movement of energy however small, sometimes it is just a little which helps to tip the balance in favour of a good outcome. The greatest problem facing mankind is how to reverse global warming, at least that part of it for which man is responsible. We depend for life upon the purity of the Earth's atmosphere, its pollution threatens our continued existence on the planet. That fresh oxygen layer of atmosphere, upon which our survival depends, needs to be cherished as our greatest treasure. One writer has suggested that we are using the atmosphere as one great sewage dump, difficult to imagine, when we think we are seeing clear, clean air. Yet that air is increasingly tainted by the vibrations of invisible emanations from pollutants which are so sophisticated, but which are lethal in their ability to poison and destroy the delicate invisible structure of Nature's protective life gift of air to humanity.

We may underestimate the effect of the vibration of our own out-breath on the atmosphere. Whether we breathe out through the mouth or nose, does matter, for mouth exhalation contains quite a lethal cocktail of pollutant gas, which we believe is meant to be purified at the back of the throat before exhaling through the nose. It is similar to the action of the analytic converter, which purifies the exhaust fumes before leaving the exhaust pipe of a car.

Those who breathe wrongly, think wrongly, therefore must act wrongly, even unconsciously. It is the collective action of mankind springing from our collective negative thought, via incorrect breathing producing incorrect action against nature, which is basically the cause of global warming.

Research needs to be done on an issue such as this, i.e. the degree of pollutant in nasal versus mouth exhalation. Such research would not be costly, but results might be dramatic, introducing a more natural way in which we can personally help the Earth. The better we breathe the kinder we become to ourselves and others, the result of being more calm and confident. It seems natural to extend this kindness to the Earth upon which we depend for life.

Correct breathing helps to restore our sense of wonder at the natural marvels around us. To study ourselves more and more in a thoughtful way, not in criticism, but to use our growing sense of importance to the world by way of developing gifts and skills we know we have but have never yet used, and have been acting like a doormat, as if we did not matter. If we don't think we matter, we don't think other people matter, it shows up in our relationships and work, and we miss so much fun.

Some of the ideas in this lecture may lead you to discover more about the wonderful world of interesting facts about breathing, and perhaps future training in subjects you did not know existed! Follow your intuition, the world is changing, and old incorrect thinking about how we have to conquer Nature is no longer appropriate.

One of the most important aspects of breathing correctly, is the cultivation of reflective thinking i.e., thoughtfulness. We may question many things we have been doing automatically, irrespective of whether or not they were in our best interests. We may realise that we have been thinking as others expect us to think, even thinking and believing their thoughts had to be our own, which is very boring and does not allow our own minds to develop. With correct breathing we become a container for fresh correct thinking about what is right for us, and accept only that as our new guideline. In so doing we can hurt no-one. Almost every aspect of our lives comes up for scrutiny, how we use or waste time, how and what we eat, our relationships, our work, even our addictions. We are all addicted to something, often something it is now safe to jettison.

> The game of life is the game of boomerangs. Our thoughts, deeds and words return to us sooner or later, with astounding accuracy.
>
> *Florence Scovel-Shinn*

Good to imagine you are in the rowing boat of your life, throwing overboard what you don't need any more!

One of the most important ways to create a new life, is to start by having a good long sleep, then try to rest as soon as we feel depleted. The moment we try to operate when we are tired, we see everything as one writer put it 'through emotional magnifying glasses'. Another word for that is crabbit!

It takes a while before we realise that the social occasion or event we declined to attend as we were tired, turned out to be not very exciting anyway, from what our friends tell us. It takes some willpower to achieve this strength of mind and not to follow the masses, but it is surprising how often something pleasant happens to us, which we would have missed if we had 'followed the others' and not listened to our intuition.

Once you get over the feeling of guilt by resting when you are tired, you realise that you have achieved just as much, and enjoyed it more. Taking life a little more slowly, at Alpha pace, that of the earth, improves our reflective ability, and often gives birth to great and exciting ideas. These are the things which makes life much more interesting because they probably come from your heart, and the resultant action benefits everyone.

You may go on to take the Great Big Trust's Teacher Training Course. **The Celtic people insisted that only poets should be teachers. Why? They said that "knowledge not taught from the heart is dangerous".**

Howard Kent in his book *Breathe Better, Feel Better* says: "The heart is the most powerful force of electrical generation in the body - its beat is linked to the state of brain and mind via the respiration. Frustration and resentment, which often do not produce a strong external appearance, result in harsh and harmful changes within the heart."

Reading the ample media coverage of heart disease in its numerous forms, suffered by so many thousands, particularly in big cities, it is so sad to understand the amount of sheer misery constantly experienced by a large proportion of the population.

The continued internalised tension experienced by hundreds of thousands in our big cities can only be reduced if the emotional and spiritual reasons for such unhappiness are acknowledged and addressed. The quickest and best way to reduce heart pressure is to amplify our natural sense of self-love, which becomes the direct and most important symptom of correct breathing. It would seem that the only proper and wholesome alternative to the needles, knives and tablets of our respected medical professions are an army of Correct Breathers. As one young Glasgow woman said after a session of breathing and relaxation, **"What we need are Spiritual gladiators."**

As we repair our breathing, we may notice stirrings around the heart area as we regularly and naturally lift the breath from the bottom to the top of the lungs. Each correct breath is another step in perfecting the circulation. The heart area is of course the great railway station for the exchange of clean and used air, and of all the organs, the effect of breath correction has a profoundly beneficial effect on the heart. Improved circulation gives us a feeling that the heart is warmer, we are opening up, becoming warmer hearted. No longer a candidate for later life heart surgery, our improved brain oxygen stops us joining the queue for Alzheimer's or senile dementia, it looks as if you are going to have fun until you drop! You'll be using your brain, vibration, electrical energy, self-healing, wonderful aura, and best of all correct breathing to be a living example to others, and Mother Nature will love you as her own !

Nature never did betray the heart that loved her

William Wordsworth

* * *

Testimonials from people who have benefited through using Correct Breathing

"A wonderful opportunity."
"Very open and friendly."
"Very interesting and thought-provoking."
"Breathing correctly makes me feel stronger and walk faster."

Comments made by participants of a Correct Breathing Workshop

Learning to breathe correctly got me through
my exams, got a B1.

Student who had contemplated dropping out of her course.

I realised today how I hide my light from myself
and relearning correct breathing has re-affirmed my
courage to be who I truly am.

Anne

Forgot how good correct breathing is.
I found the class very useful, it reminded me that I EXIST,
I need to take more time for me."

Isa

Very good and easy to understand.
I felt so calm and relaxed. My chest feels so open and free!!!

Margaret

Excellent, I love relaxation. It is a treat.

Kim

* * *

Excerpt from Student Essay

GREAT BIG TRUST, LEVEL 7 INTRODUCTION TO CORRECT BREATHING COURSE

Mental and emotional health are also deeply connected to the breath. It has been accepted for some time now that emotional memory is also stored in the soft tissues of the body as well as in the memory banks of the brain. A poor and inadequate respiratory pattern will ensure that unresolved and unconscious emotional issues and traumas remain locked into the body, causing all kinds of physical symptoms, ranging from muscular tensions and chronic aches and pains, stiffness, frozen shoulders and arthritis, to cancers and life-threatening illness and disease.

Bernadette

What other Visionary Writers have said about Breathing and Life

Teachers who are able to produce relaxation instead of tension in their pupils are amazed by the improvement in their work. In every case, grades go up and the child's approach to his work is different, keener, more alert.

Karin Roon, The New Way to Relax

If teachers and parents were aware of the tremendous gain of knowing about breathing control and the effect of sudden breath changes in keeping discipline, this knowledge would be taught in all colleges.

Karin Roon, The New Way to Relax

* * *

If we can accept that there is a right and a wrong way to breathe, why are the children not breathing properly? If you challenge me – do some research – check out the children in all the classrooms in Glasgow, the children's homes, the hospitals. Most of them are choosing to begin to die by the age of eight. Our classrooms are full of death choices (including the teachers). So are the children's homes, most of them. What about Trade Union Meetings if it comes to that, the places of Government, the Churches, the Medical Profession!? Have the leaders rejected life within themselves? One only has to observe the breathing pattern. How then can they give life to those they 'lead'? Doctors have the biggest suicide and alcoholism rate of all the professions, but aren't they supposed to give us life? And yet, and yet –

Anne Gillard Shearer, LOVE, DRUGS... or any city like Glasgow

In the face of this call to develop children as persons, it seems important to me that we recognise clearly just how de-personalising our society, our schools and our own relationships are... It seems clear to me that our schools are overly intellectualising, and that this bias which begins even in the nursery school turns 'good' secondary schools into academic factories and many teachers into custodians of an examination system with many children refugees of the same system. For those who cannot cope on an obvious personal level a heartless scientific psychiatry dominates our hospitals.'

R. Carlisle, Experiential Religious Education

Go into any Children's Home administered by any agency, and you will find appalling levels of incorrect breathing in the children. Appalling too is the bad breathing of their educators and carers – an ongoing cycle of fear, tension, bad communications and acting out behaviour by both sides, camouflaged by frightening levels of bureaucracy and 'paper diaorrhea' while the child's spirit dies.

Recalling the phrase 'Teaching a young child to breathe correctly is like giving water to a dying daffodil.' There are 'dying daffodils' in all our classroom and children's homes and no one notices.

Not all the Specialists, the Doctors, the psychologists, psychiatrists, the counsellors.

Anne Gillard Shearer, LOVE, DRUGS... or any city like Glasgow

When I went to the physiotherapist for breathing retraining, my daughter took me with her nine-year-old son – my grandson – who was off school. It was really funny seeing how we all breathed alike, and had little habits the same. We all had disordered patterns – all three generations.

Dinah Bradley, Hyperventilation Syndrome

Negative thoughts weigh heavily on the abdomen and disrupt its proper functioning. The body is isolated from the mind and the rupture between the two brains is total.

Pierre Pallardy,
Gut Instinct - What your stomach is trying to tell you

The most radical part of learning to nose-breathe again was I could kiss properly. My boyfriend pointed out to me that kissing me used to be like kissing a gasping goldfish. And it's made the rest of my sex life so much better too, because I feel so much better. I hadn't realised what I was missing out on.

Dinah Bradley, Hyperventilation Syndrome

The heart is the most powerful force of electrical generation in the body - its beat is linked to the state of brain and mind via the respiration. Frustration and resentment, which often do not produce a strong external appearance, result in harsh and harmful changes within the heart.

Pierre Pallardy,
Gut Instinct - What your stomach is trying to tell you

* * *

Affirmations

AN AFFIRMATION IS A POSITIVE STATEMENT OF ABSOLUTE TRUTH. REPEAT IT TO YOURSELF OR WRITE IT OUT TO RE-AFFIRM SOMETHING THAT YOU WANT TO BECOME TRUE

It is okay for me to have what I want.

The universe loves and supports me.

I relax and allow life to flow.

I am loved just for being myself.

There is enough for everyone.

Being true to myself is being true to everyone.

I am only addicted to loving myself, nothing has power over me.

People love me when I say 'no'.

Inspirational quotes to help on your Breathing Journey

The heart that breaks open can contain the whole universe.

Jaonne Macy

When seeking revenge, dig two graves.

Chinese proverb

People living deeply have no fear of death.

Anais Nin

* * *

Paradise is always where love dwells.

Richter

Wherever you go, go with all your heart.

Confucius

We choose our joys and sorrows long before we experience them.

Kahlil Gibran

A good head and a good heart are always a formidable combination.

Nelson Mandela

In the sweetness of friendship let there be laughter, and sharing of pleasures. For in the dew of little things, the heart finds its morning and is refreshed.

Khalil Gibran

Faith is an oasis in the heart which will never be reached. by the caravan of thinking

Khalil Gibran

There is a wisdom of the head, and a wisdom of the heart.

Charles Dickens

A kiss makes the heart young again and wipes out the years.

Rupert Brooke

Accept the things to which fate binds you, and love the people with whom fate brings you together, but do so with all your heart.

Marcus Aurelius

* * *

There never was any heart truly great and generous,
was not also tender and compassionate.

Robert Frost

A loving heart is the beginning of all knowledge.

Thomas Carlyle

A torn jacket is soon mended; but hard words bruise the
heart of a child.

Henry Longfellow

The voyage of discovery lies not in finding new landscapes
but in having new eyes.

Marcel Proust

* * *

PART TEN

The Environment

IT IS OBVIOUSLY an excellent development that we are universally becoming conscious of the lethal effect which some of mankind's inventions are having upon the earth. A great deal of this awareness is focused upon the pollution of our atmosphere, that layer of life-giving air which is really such a narrow band surrounding the earth that we might liken to a coat of varnish upon a thick piece of wood. So much of the concern is with the effects that we can see in visual terms from that which is man-made. As we have already pointed out in this book the effects of an energy which we cannot see but which when used incorrectly, our breath, must also have an effect on the environment. It is understood that we process about 11,000 litres of air a day through our lungs. We might take a moment to think of the quality of the 11,000 litres which if breathed 'in' correctly will also be breathed 'out' correctly via the exhale, and be less of a pollutant. It has been suggested elsewhere that at the back of the throat there is a mechanism similar to the catalytic converter on the car's exhaust, which purifies the air as it leaves the nose in the same way that the catalytic converter purifies the emissions from the exhaust pipe before they pollute the atmosphere.

70% of the waste material from our bodies is excreted via our out-breath, 3% of solids, 7% as urine and 20% as perspiration. When our human catalytic converter works on our exhale in correct breathing, the resultant purification process ensures that this emanation is benign.

When we breathe incorrectly, the conversion process is unable to deal with the concentration of toxic and carbon waste being released which is then discharged into the atmosphere in an un-refined form. It therefore must pay dividends in our material efforts to save the environment to consider the effect of the pollution of our environment by the way we breathe?

Could this be a deciding factor in acknowledging the as yet unrecognised power we have to heal the planet by our breathing. The planet can only be healed when man becomes spiritually mature and after all the words breath and spirit are synonymous.

We acknowledge the cleansing effect of plant-life in the conversion of carbon dioxide to oxygen but realise that the balance of people breathing incorrectly with toxic exhale put the plant kingdom under pressure so that it cannot complete the cycle of conversion. This does not take into the equation the mass cutting down of trees etc by man, remembering that the Rain Forests are the 'lungs of the earth'.

Our exhale is therefore capable of polluting the atmosphere depending upon whether we breathe correctly or not. If you consider a city of three million adults, over 341 million litres of exhaled air flows out into the atmosphere daily, which will either be polluted or unpolluted depending on the respiratory efficiency of the inhabitants. This has to be purified in some way, so that it can be re-inhaled in a cleansed form. If the available atmospheric layer becomes too heavily poisoned from the effects of pollutants such as fossil fuel emissions, green-house gasses, etc, etc, is it realistic to imagine a time not too far distant when it will only be possible to breathe in air full of such pollution, which in turn have a lethal effect on our lungs, brain and bloodstream.

It would be difficult to deny that only a spiritual revolution can be the answer to the problems of the world.

This broad vision of understanding what could be man's salvation is developing naturally from the thoughts of many as they correct their breathing. It is an amazing coincidence that this is happening, because the information is not being given from the media or an outside source, but arising from a universal inner wisdom yet to be acknowledged... Is there still time ?

As mentioned earlier, the renowned scientist Albert Einstein believed in the existence of a fourth dimension or higher consciousness of man which can never be proved within any present scientific theory because of the limitations of science. The over-emphasis of left brain thinking within scientific training might well be blocking the scientific world from entering a quantum shift in thought dimension, which may have to admit to the existence of Einstein's fourth dimension of higher consciousness.

Pollutants continue to spill into the air we breathe, especially in cities where there are fumes from car exhausts which settle into the grids of streets and roads that make up urban settlements. Poor ventilation in public buildings also places the lungs and the human respiratory system under stress. A random survey of schools, public buildings, shops and hospitals reveals a complete lack of proper ventilation and fresh air renewal. Indeed many buildings have no windows that actually open, and rely upon poor and inadequate air-conditioning systems. Health and Safety needs to greatly widen its scope of awareness and willingness to take action in improving the quality of air in these buildings. Many public buildings are also over-heated, allowing the stale air to carry and multiply air borne-bacteria. The lack of ventilation in such buildings also means that we breathe in a soup of other people's exhale. Nature never intended it to be like this; good fresh air, which is free, is a natural part of our ability to stay healthy and vital.

The following diagrams illustrate the effect our breathing and our brain balance has on nature and the environment we live in. As we become less aware of our breathing and slip further into 'poor breathing' with an over-reliance on left brain analytical thinking, rampant materialism and consumerism, we begin to lose the life-giving sense of our relationship with nature. In effect we plunder nature with little regard to ecological balance and nature of course has to take the necessary steps to protect and re-balance herself. Hence as our breathing deteriorates so does the environment we live in. This process could well be reversible. Improvement in breathing leads to an improved natural environment, and also allows more creative flexibility, to adapt with environmental change.

Air, light and rest were a big part of the treatment regime in

CORRECT BREATHING - 100% BREATHING
The Model of Health on All Levels
Creative, Spiritual, Loving, In Touch with Nature
* Recognises, Values, Uses Own Talents & Skills
* Left & Right Brain Balance
* Healthy - Full of Energy - Self Healing
* Life in Harmony with Breath
* Confident, Self Aware, Nurtured,
* Innate Sense of Self
* Balanced Masculine & Feminine

Reduction in
Correct Breathing

100% Breathing - Life is Good and Growing

CORRECT BREATHING PRACTICE CAN REVERSE DECLINE

50% Breathing - Losing the Connection with Breath & Nature - Things Breaking Up
* Stressed and Stressful Living
* Illness and Disease Based Medical Model
* Difficulty in Self Healing & Staying Healthy
* Tired and Run Down
* Left Brain Dominating
* Struggling in a Heavily Materialistic Society

20% Breathing - Connection with Breath & Nature Almost Gone - Very Limited Breathing
* Nature is Deserted - Ability to Self Heal Lost
* Artificial Living & Robotic Life Pattern
* Lost Sight of Talents and Relationship to Self
* No Positive Vision - Strife, Fear, Conflict Rule
* Reliance on Medically Prescribed Drugs
* Alcohol and Substance Use and Abuse

CORRECT BREATHING PRACTICE CAN REVERSE THE DECLINE IN HEALTH & LIFE and LEAD AGAIN TO A FULL, GOOD, RICH & REWARDING LIFE

RELATIONSHIP OF BREATH TO SELF, NATURE & LIFE

MAN, BREATH AND NATURE

hospitals for TB (Tuberculosis) which is on the rise again. Could a contributory factor for its re-emergence be poor air quality in buildings?

The rise of the supply of small commercial oxygen inhalers and oxygen bars in heavily trafficked, industrialised and congested city areas such as in Tokyo, Japan, is a salutary reminder of the effect of the anti-natural oxygen depleted atmosphere in urban areas which seriously reduces the essential availability of pure air for survival. Existing signs of awareness and efforts to deal with this disease of the air in large cities all over the world are seriously lacking.

An American doctor, Dr. L. Burns, who examined the blood specimens of more than 20,000 people to discover the affect of carbon monoxide on the body, wrote: "Carbon monoxide gas (a waste product of petrol found in car exhaust) seeps into the blood through the lungs, and mixes with the haemoglobin to such an extent that the blood cannot perform its normal function of carrying oxygen to the rest of the body."

A French professor stated that the liver needs a great deal of oxygen. its enemies being acid, alcohol and nicotine. Its one major ally is oxygen. But someone who breathes incorrectly will be unable to supply the liver with its oxygen requirement.

It would seem that pollution by sound and car exhausts, frequently a major polluting factor in cities has been replaced by a pollutant electrical excretion at Beta rhythm, 15 - 25 cycles a second. This is the vibration being excreted into the atmosphere by the combined vibrational force from millions of electrically charged appliances and equipment; TVs, neon lighting, street lighting, sound systems, home appliances, etc., all of which constitute via the build up of Beta waves, an oxygen destructive atmosphere in the air within, around and above the city. This constant high pitched energy is an invisible destroyer of life on a level which science has yet to acknowledge.

Unrelenting high pitched noise is also a vibrational pollutant factor. Motorways rarely stop, and have a damaging effect on the human sensory system and are unseen tension creators which take its toll on our health.

A COURSE IN COURAGE

Respiratory efficiency	Negative thought patterns	Fear	Calm Peace Love Joy	Nasties! Addictions Self Hate Guilt Unforgive-ness Envy Greed Jealousy Malice and sadness	Circulatory efficiency Cell oxygen distribution How I will choose to die My 'death' wish	Mental Physical Emotional & Spiritual imbalance Also including the sexual	Approve of myself and my fellow man
%	%	%	%	%	%	%	%
10	90	90	10	90	10	90	10
20	80	80	20	80	20	80	20
30	70	70	30	70	30	70	30
40	60	60	40	60	40	60	40
50	50	50	50	50	50	50	50
60	40	40	60	40	60	40	60
70	20	30	70	30	70	30	60
80	20	20	80	20	80	20	80
90	10	10	90	10	90	10	90
100	0	0	100	0	100	0	100

The above headings also reflect our over domination of brain activity either of the left or right hemisphere.
This chart forms part of the "Course for the Courageous" by Anne Shearer.

The city can be likened to a 24/7 obscene feeding machine which destroys oxygen and whose harsh environment is unnatural and harmful to humans.

Man-made materials don't breathe.

The suffocating effect of the city and built up areas chokes the earth's ability to breathe and to re-generate itself. Man-made material, such as concrete in buildings or nylon based clothing fabrics don't breathe, thus preventing the circulation of air within whatever they enclose.

We know that violent bahaviour is endemic, but also the violent deaths of thousands if not millions through the predominant respiratory, heart and lung diseases and cancers can also be seen as tragic manifestations of violence, in the sense that we have violated the natural laws of nature in preventing ourselves from breathing correctly and healing ourselves. These manifestations of violence can be linked to both the outer and inner environments and are signs that both systems are under extreme stress.

A widespread and active public debate needs to be begun on the big issues of human health, plant health, animal health and the health of the planet we live on. In all cases things have become out of balance because we have ignored the importance of nature's rules on breathing correctly, and the urgent and vital need to have a positive and creative relationship with nature. Remembering Wordsworth's lines: "Nature never did betray the heart that loved her." Einstein also stated that the real question that faces man is "is nature friendly?"

To requote Theodore Roszak: "There is no mental health in our cities until we reawaken our psychic links with Nature." Roszak argues, suggesting that our very earliest subconscious awareness is about such ties, which are deeper even than our much explored relationship with our mothers. Pre-scientific people knew and felt this; to be healthy we must learn again to be as intimately aware of trees and mountains and animals as we are of our human relations. Children know this naturally observed Wordsworth, "until shades of the prison house close in".

The presence of fear can be recognised by anyone trained in

breath awareness. Limitation of breathing through fear leads to a deterioration in our circulation, and lack of oxygen to the blood. This inevitably leads to physical, mental and emotional dis-ease. The reversal of these symptoms simply means the reversal of incorrect breathing and the re-instatement of correct breathing and restoration of good health.

Breathing correctly leads to deep relaxation and feelings of love for ourself and others.

The above process can be evaluated within the simple chart 'A Course in Courage' on page 174. Connecting a percentage of respiratory limitation, or emotional fear, with the resultant knock on negative effect in other areas. The chart indicates overall improvements that come about with Correct Breathing.

Whilst the chart is self-explanatory, it would be worthwhile for several like-minded people to study it, and become fully aware of its truth. There is no escaping the truth.

There are many reasons why we become afraid, and almost without exception they begin in childhood. Maturity involves evolving through the percentage levels of stress we place upon our breathing until, once again, it has been restored to its intended perfection, and therefore fully functioning on all four cylinders.

Are you prepared to take this risk of trust? It may take months of gradual change until we are once again back to normal.

Testimonials from people who have benefited through using Correct Breathing

I live in the country, but occasionally travel to a big city where I stay for several days in connection with research work. I find when I return home that for several days I experience nasal congestion and the need to frequently clear my nose and throat of mucus, which does not happen when I am at home.

I have come to the conclusion that during my post city clearance of toxins I am excreting pollutants from city air which are of course experienced daily by city residents. Another name for the phenomena is 'city pox'.

Country dweller

I know of a small family, parents and two children, who, although living in the country, seem to have continual rounds of colds and flu-like symptoms. The parents work from home and are not away from the house much but the children attend a school which is very poorly ventilated and stuffy, and which can be the only source of these frequent colds. It seems that this is common to many schools, with children bringing infections home with them. It also highlights the need for less use of antibiotics, giving the children a natural opportunity to build up their immune systems to enable them to fight off these bugs.

Family friend

"I don't get so angry", "Concentrating on my breathing helps me calm my mind", "It helps me sleep", "I think it helps me listen more", "I notice how my breath helps me".

Comments by children after being introduced to correct breathing.

I took a taxi to meet up with my colleague with whom I was working on this book. Got chatting to the taxi driver, he asked me what I was doing and I told him about the book and a bit about breathing. He thanked me brightly and said he'd found our chat very interesting. About a month later I found myself arriving at the same location for more of the same work, got into a taxi to be greeted by the same man who clearly remembered our previous conversation. He told me he'd been practicing the breathing exercise I'd given him and was pleased to know we'd progressed with the book. He put in an order for the book!

Over the years I have had numerous conversations about breathing with people in chance meetings, they all seemed very interested in, and animated by the topic, I think this is because we all have a strong and intuitive sense about the quality of our breathing and its importance to our well-being.

Co-compiler of this book

What other Visionary Writers have said about Breathing and Life

It was only in 1924 that a group of Physicians working at the St. Louis Infirmary, in co-operation with Washington University, concluded from their study of 1,000 persons, that better health and longer life for middle-aged people may be achieved by 'maintaining the proper level of oxygen consumption in the body'.

Hilton Hotima

The nearer you live to a large city, the more likely you are to go insane. These are the conclusions of a study of the Geography of Insanity in five large cities of the USA. The rate of lunacy lessens as you travel from the centre of the city.

Hilton Hotima

The former Canadian Prime Minister, Pierre Trudeau, in speaking to the United Nations quoted from a passage in which the Scientist-Priest, Pierre Teillhard de Chardin urged a 'conspiracy of love'. Conspiracy in its literal meaning is 'to breathe together'

When it is known that one takes about 30 cubic inches of air into one's lungs in each inhalation, or about seven times the weight of food and water consumed, it can be understood why more people are weakened, devitalised and poisoned by pollution in the air they suck into their lungs, than by all the ingredients in the food we eat and the water we drink.

The Mellon Institute of Industrial Research

Do you hold your breath half of the time? Did you realize some people hold their breath in, while others hold out?

Typically, those of us who tend constantly to be rushing around, trying to do a great deal in their lives, are the ones who breathe in and then hold their breath there. They forget to breathe out, or even feel they haven't got time to do so. They thus push themselves through life on an inbreath. Theirs tend to be lives lived in a constant pattern of stress.

Jenny Beeken, Don't Hold Your Breath

Disease associated with holding breath in:

High blood pressure, heart disease, tension, migraine, headaches, angina; all stress-related diseases.

Disease associated with holding breath out:

Low blood pressure, multiple sclerosis, depression, ME (fatigue syndrome), lack of energy for life.

Jenny Beeken, Don't Hold Your Breath

It is really only since the 1980's that the scientific community has become aware and has started to alert us about the risk of overloading the atmosphere with greenhouse gases and upsetting our planet's climatological balance.

Jan de Vries, Air, The Breath of Life

Carbon Dioxide, CO_2, which is a colourless, odourless substance is the most prevalent greenhouse gas. Industrialisation in the North has made a great contribution to CO_2 emissions and we now live with the threat of increased CO_2 emissions from the developing Third World also.

Jan de Vries, Air, The Breath of Life

Never mistake motion for progress.

Mark Twain

* * *

There has never been a time, in any society in any part of the world, without its sages and teachers to challenge materialism and plead for a different order of priorities...Today, however, this message reaches us not solely from the sages and saints but from the actual course of physical events. It speaks to us in the language of terrorism, genocide, breakdown, pollution, exhaustion.

Everywhere people ask: "What can I actually do?" The answer is as simple as it is disconcerting: we can, each of us, work to put our own inner house in order. The guidance we need for this work cannot be found in science or technology, the value of which utterly depends on the ends they serve; but it can still be found in the traditional wisdom of mankind.

E. F. Schumacher, Small is Beautiful

Parental Messages

Did you get any of these messages from your parents? If you did, correcting your breathing will help to cancel out their negative effect. There are many more messages which you may have received and which are still having a negative effect on your life, breathe them out and let them go forever. Create your own positive messages and affirmations to yourself. You are beautiful, complete and whole.

You need help

I want you to stay young

You come last

Please others

Nothing is secret

Children are to be seen and not heard

Drop dead

Why don't you ever do anything right?

Affirmations

AN AFFIRMATION IS A POSITIVE STATEMENT OF ABSOLUTE TRUTH. REPEAT IT TO YOURSELF OR WRITE IT OUT TO RE-AFFIRM SOMETHING THAT YOU WANT TO BECOME TRUE

I stand on my own two feet

I love and appreciate myself

My life is filled with love

I love what I see in me
My body loves to be healthy

I am healthier than I have ever been
Every cell in my body is loved

I love my body

I feel at one with all of life

Life supports me at every turn

I have all the time in the world

Inspirational quotes to help on your Breathing Journey

A person starts to live when he can live outside of himself

Albert Einstein

Every minute you are angry, you lose sixty seconds of happiness

Ralph Waldo Emerson

The best thing about the future is that
it comes only one day at a time.

Abraham Lincoln

Cheerfulness is as natural to the heart of a man in
strong health as colour is to his cheeks.

John Ruskin

If I keep a green bough in my heart, the singing bird will come.

Chinese Proverb

I love laughing.

William Blake

One joy scatters a hundred griefs.

Chinese Proverb

There is sufficiency in the world for man's need
but not for man's greed.

Gandhi

To live a pure unselfish life, one must count nothing
as one's own in the midst of abundance

Buddha

When one tugs at a single thing in nature, he finds it
attached to the rest of the world

John Muir

The control man has secured over nature has far
outrun his control over himself

Ernest Jones

* * *

On the Anatomy and Physiology of the Respiratory System

THE ILLUSTRATED *Anatomy and Physiology of Breathing* which forms this appendix is a booklet for those who want to study the physical workings of the respiratory system in a simple form. It is followed by a fun questionnaire in a multiple choice format which you may wish to share with friends or in a group.

Section One of the questionnaire requires that you tick the incorrect answer out of the four questions and in Section Two you are asked to tick the correct answer.

Some of the answers may surprise you; the correct answers are contained within the main text of the booklet.

THE GREAT BIG TRUST

THE GLOBAL RESPIRATORY EDUCATIONAL ADVANCEMENT TRUST

Helpful Information and Basic Interesting Facts
on the Anatomy and Physiology of the
Respiratory System

INTRODUCTION

This little booklet contains the information and diagrams that you will need to know in order to successfully complete the multiple choice questions on the third day of Level 7 i.e. on 10th September 2011.

It contains basic important information on the Anatomy and Physiology of Correct Breathing and its relation to our well-being.

The Multiple Choice question test makes up 30% of your overall course marks.

Within this booklet we have only included the facts that will be helpful for you to absorb in order that you understand your own personal progress through experiencing the very practical aspect of Correct Breathing.

The facts within this booklet make a good basis of information you can share with others with whom you may go on to practice Correct Breathing.

Please note that the Multiple Choice Test comes in two sections. Each question has four possible answers.

The Multiple Choice Test
In Section 1 you will be asked to tick the incorrect answer and in Section 2 you will be asked to tick the correct answer.

BEST AGE FOR CORRECT BREATHING

We know most about breathing at birth.
The healthy baby is the perfect instructor in breathing and relaxation.

A healthy baby is the perfect instructor in breathing and relaxation. Watch it and see why. The new-born child uses all the muscles of its trunk that should be involved in the breathing process, those of the abdomen, sides and back.

There is no habit in life that pays bigger dividends, and pays them more promptly, than complete breathing. It is the source of your health, your cheerful spirits, your feeling of youth, your energy and your relaxation.

Karin Roon, The New Way to Relax 2nd Ed.,
Glasgow: Phoenix (Scotland) Publishers (1991), p.47

The muscles are relaxed and have not gathered tension. The baby is close to nature and the natural functioning of the body.

Be aware of your breath as often as you are able. Do this for a year, and it will be more powerfully transformative than all other courses you can attend - and it's free.

Eckhart Tolle

PHYSICAL ACTION OF CORRECT BREATHING

In order to breathe correctly we first have to expand the lower part of the lungs.
If a person is breathing correctly the expansion can be seen starting from below the rib cage rising up through the chest to the upper lobes of the lungs, just below the collar bone.

There will be no sign of any pulling in or blocking this fluid movement. The shoulders themselves do not rise. If the lower abdomen is pulled in at the start of the breath it is because muscles are blocking (through fear) the full lung expansion.

The chest cavity of a correct breather is full and broad.
An incorrect breather may develop a chest cavity which is narrow, long, sagging and cold.

The muscular structure of the body can carry tension and this tension can restrict the breathing pattern.

A healthy baby has little tension and its breathing pattern is full and free.

As a person re-educates themselves in correct breathing, the circulation improves and so muscles and skeletal structure are properly nourished, the lungs open out, ridding themselves of toxins, become healthy full and broad. This process of development is able to continue, allowing the inhale and exhale to be full and rhythmic.

The way we breathe reveals a lot about our general outlook on life.How much and how freely we breathe reflects how willing we are to meet life around us. How we exhale shows how willing we are to trust what happens to us and to go with the flow of life.

G. Minett, Exhale: An Overview of Breath Work
Great Britain: Floris Books (2004), p21

BREATH IS LIFE!

Eminent authorities have stated that one generation of correct breathers would regenerate the race and disease would be so rare as to be looked upon as a curiosity.

Yogi Ramacharaka, The Science of Breath
London: L. N. Fowler & Co. Ltd. (2005), p9

Correct breathing supplies adequate oxygen to the cells and warms the air as it enters the nose, filters the air before it enters the lungs and the old air containing CO_2 is discharged via the nose.

It is natural to breathe in and out through the nose.
The nose is the main organ for breathing, a fact that is often not given enough importance.

If a person does not use their nose for breathing, often it becomes clogged and congested, and they continue to use their mouth.

* * *

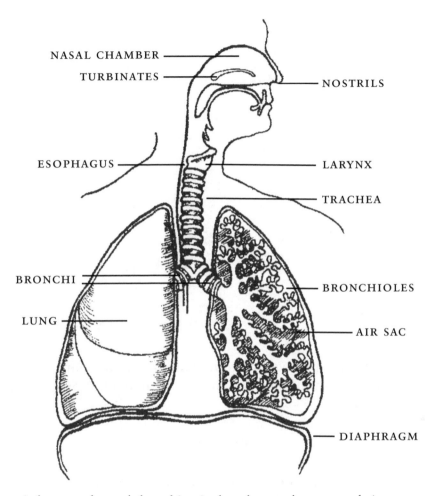

NASAL CHAMBER

TURBINATES

NOSTRILS

ESOPHAGUS

LARYNX

TRACHEA

BRONCHI

BRONCHIOLES

LUNG

AIR SAC

DIAPHRAGM

A feature of mouth-breathing is that the nasal passages, being thus comparatively unused, consequently fail to keep themselves clean and clear, and become clogged up and unclean, and are apt to contract local diseases. Like abandoned roads that soon become filled with weeds and rubbish, unused nostrils become filled with impurities and foul matter.

Yogi Ramacharaka, The Science of Breath
London: L. N. Fowler & Co. Ltd. (2005), p25

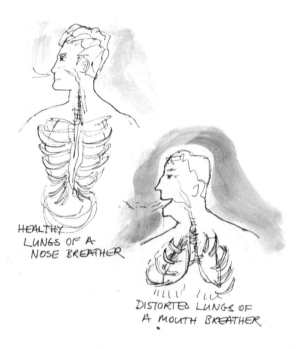

HEALTHY
LUNGS OF A
NOSE BREATHER

DISTORTED LUNGS OF
A MOUTH BREATHER

Prolonged passive breathing and mouth breathing can cause the nostril to shrink in size, limiting the amount of oxygen getting to the brain.

THE BRAIN

30 to 40% of our total oxygen is required by the brain
The brain is oxygen hungry and needs 30 to 40% of our oxygen intake to function well, if it doesn't get this it will start to go into stressful short beta wave rhythms, like an engine over-heating.

Symptoms of health associated with correct breathing are good circulation, less requirement for artificial heat, more energy, as energy is no longer being diverted to maintain muscular and brain tension.

The sense that a person can feel their body run cold with fear indicates that fear has held their muscles tense, and the circulation of blood and oxygen has been compromised.

The healthy and complete exhale is important as without this the body will hold onto waste materials and toxins which in time build up and create disease. Many people through uncertainty, insecurity and fear hold onto the exhale, and it is not completed, thereby retaining toxins and phlegm in the system.

The best way to ensure that a full and correct breath is taken in is to make sure that all the old air has been exhaled i.e. that the lungs have properly completed the exhaled.

Breathing is one of the bodily functions which is voluntary and involuntary. This means we can change our breathing pattern, it is something that can be worked on and improved, thus improving the overall health of the individual.

Changing the way we Breathe (changing it to Correct Breathing) can change the way our brain works - and give us conscious control over our blood pressure, immune system, mental and spiritual health.

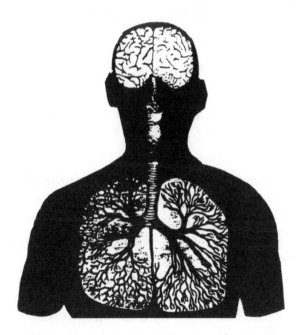

DIAPHRAGMATIC ACTION

The diaphragm muscle is located just below the rib cage at the base of the chest.
It is shaped like a dome and lowers and flattens as we breathe in. This creates space allowing the base of the lungs to expand.

As we breathe out the diaphragm and rib cage relaxes as the old air is squeezed out.

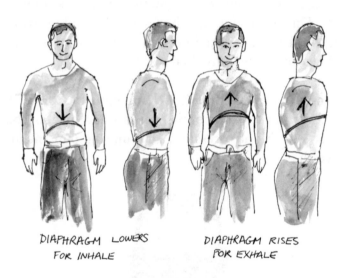

DIAPHRAGM LOWERS FOR INHALE

DIAPHRAGM RISES FOR EXHALE

DIAPHRAGM MOVING UP AND DOWN
THE BODY ON EXHALE AND INHALE.

Symptoms of health associated with Correct Breathing are good circulation, less requirement for artificial heat and more energy.
The oxygen rich blood is flowing freely around the body with little muscular tension restricting it, the elimination of toxins via the blood and the exhale are unimpeded.

The quality of blood depends upon its proper oxygenation
Breathing is the way in which we transport oxygen from the air to our body's cells, where it is used to burn carbohydrates, proteins

and fats, thus releasing the energy that keeps us going. It is also the way in which we rid our bodies of a by-product of the combustion process, carbon dioxide.

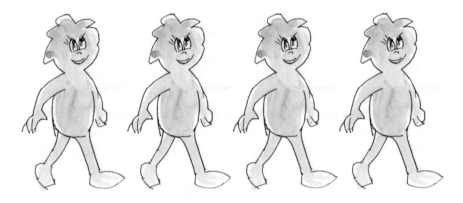

BUSY BLOOD MOLECULES

Healthy lung tissue will resist germs
When we breathe correctly our blood and oxygen circulation is improved through the action of the lungs. The inhale brings in fresh oxygen and the exhale gives out carbon dioxide and expels toxins from the body.

As you might expect, it is not only the lung tissue that remains healthy with Correct Breathing but every cell in the body will remain healthy also.

To explore this a little further, correct breathing requires the full use of the diaphragm. The stomach, liver and reproductive organs lie beneath the diaphragm and also move when we breathe.

The breathing movement massages these organs ensuring that they receive the oxygen and adequate nutrients they require to function in a healthy way. When a person uses upper chest breathing these organs lose this benefit and function is impaired.

The lymphatic duct travels alongside the spine at the back of the thoracic cage. Movement of this region is crucial for circulation within the lymphatic system -as this regulates our immune system it is a very important function. A good breathing pattern will move the fluid in a regular, rhythmical way. Irregular patterns may cause the fluid to stagnate, leading to health problems.

Tania Clifton-Smith, Breathe to Succeed
London: Penguin Books, (1999), p.24

When we breathe correctly the lungs will create good circulation of oxygen into the blood stream. This in turn increases the effectiveness of the auto immune system and reduction of germs. The exhaled breath is important as it is said that 70% of the body's waste product, which includes germs, is exhaled through the out-breath.

A satisfactory breathing pattern is between 10 -14 breaths per minute. Our breathing varies when we are sedentary to when we are active, when we will require more intake of air because of intense muscular action requiring more oxygen.

Breathing is both a voluntary and an involuntary function which means you have conscious control over your breathing i.e. with the expression of emotion, if you are feeling stressed and think of a relaxed situation your breathing rhythm will change.

The upper lobes of the lungs are situations just beneath the clavicle or collar bone.
The lungs extend from this area down to the bottom of the rib cage at the front and back of the body.

The right lung has three lobes and the left lung has two to accommodate the heart.

The lungs inflate like a balloon, the lower inflating first then the upper lungs inflate, and on the exhale the upper then the lower lungs deflate. This should be a smooth action and not jerky - jerkyness implies musculure tension.

Like a filling a cup up with liquid, you fill from the bottom of the cup first. When emptying the cup it is from the top first.

The lowest part of the lungs are situated at the bottom of the rib cage.

THE MAIN SINUS AREAS

There are 8 holes in the bony structure of the head known as sinus cavities. Incorrect breathing disturbs the flow of oxygen through these cavities and waste toxins build up which change into mucus and block the sinus cavities.

LUNGS FILL FROM BOTTOM UP & EMPTY FROM TOP TO BOTTOM.

FILLING A CUP FROM BOTTOM UP. LIKE OUR LUNGS FILL FROM BOTTOM UP WITH AIR

EMPTYING A CUP FROM THE TOP DOWN - LIKE OUR LUNGS EMPTY FROM TOP DOWN

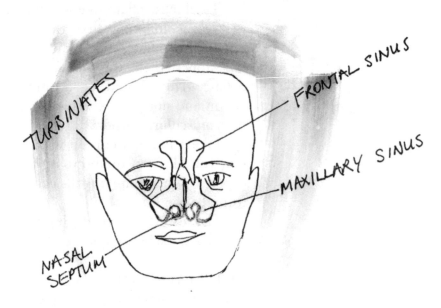

TURBINATES

FRONTAL SINUS

MAXILLARY SINUS

NASAL SEPTUM

THE MAIN SINUS AREAS ARE LOCATED ABOVE THE EYES,
THE CENTRE OF THE FOREHEAD AND SIDES OF NOSE.

The sinus cavities can become infected, causing nasal breathing and sinus headaches. Correct Breathing starts to convert the mucus into liquid which can be discharged in the natural way down the nose. The main sinus cavities are above the eyes, in the centre of the forehead, and side and base of the nose.

THE PHARYNX, LARYNX AND THE TRACHEA

The windpipe is known as the trachea, and is entered through the respiratory cavity of the pharynx at the back of the throat and larynx, (known as the voice box).

The internal exercise, which is like an internal massage, afforded by good diaphragmatic action leads to, amongst many other things, a healthy heart, clear thinking and good skin.

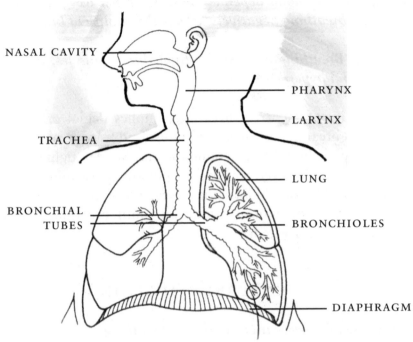

NASAL CAVITY

PHARYNX

LARYNX

TRACHEA

LUNG

BRONCHIAL TUBES

BRONCHIOLES

DIAPHRAGM

THE PHARYNX, LARYNX AND THE TRACHEA ARE ALL
CONNECTED TO THE MAIN NOSE - LUNGS PATHWAY.

INHALATION   EXHALATION

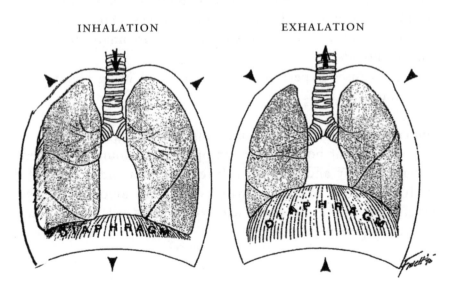

The quality of blood depends upon its proper oxygenation. Any incorrect breathing negatively affects the quality of blood.

Incorrect Breathing can lead to tight throat muscles, feelings of anxiety and hyperventilation.

The activity of incorrect breathing implies denial or rejection. Restricted breathing is caused by unresolved fear often going back to childhood. Inability to communicate the fear tightens throat muscles and unresolved fear causes rapid over-breathing or hyperventilation. The individual cannot escape from the problem which has become a permanent condition, until breathing has been naturalised or corrected.

HYPERVENTILATION

The cause of hyperventilation is over breathing.
When a person is breathing correctly, they cannot hyperventilate.

When we breathe incorrectly and meet a situation where we feel threatened our feelings of anxiety build up and we are not able to take appropriate action to defend ourselves. Our breathing rate speeds up and we take in more oxygen but are unable to expel the carbon dioxide.

This causes hyperventilation which can bring about loss of consciousness.

Imperfect breathing brings about impaired cell growth.
The cells in our body require an optimum amount of oxygen to remain healthy and to allow cell regeneration and healing of the body. Imperfect breathing, which limits the amount of oxygen circulating around the body, will not give the cells their optimum oxygen requirement.

* * *

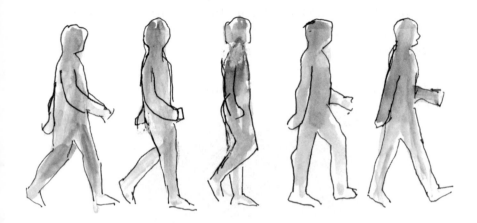

Continual Back pain can never be a symptom of correct breathing. It is true that when a person begins to breathe correctly their circulation improves and muscles that have been tense begin to relax. During this time there may be intermittent discomfort as muscles begin to heal and rid themselves of long held toxicity.

This type of discomfort is very different from the continual pain a person experiences when muscles are in distress, because of poor blood and oxygen circulation through incorrect breathing.

It is said that the muscles at the back of the eyes control around 30% of the brain's electrical activity.
Many people don't realise that the muscles at the back of the eyes lead straight to the brain.

The implications of this are huge and it means that relaxing the muscles at the back of the eyes can help the brain's electrical activity to move from a stressful beta rhythm to a calmer alpha loving rhythm.

There is also a sense that we have an inner and outer consciousness. We often forget how important it is to allow our thoughts to generate images, to visualise nice things and have pleasant memories, this is not escapism but very necessary for our well-being. We must learn to respect, trust and listen to our inner-consciousness and intuition.

How many ready made images via TV and films have violent,

harsh and stressful images which affect our brain rhythm?

A natural result of breathing correctly is the release of pleasant images into the consciousness and a deep sense of the beauty of the natural world.

It is said that the eyes are the mirrors of the soul.

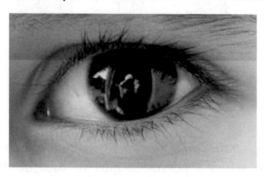

The brain stem regulates breathing through a reflex activity which occurs automatically. If you are stressed, tired or not breathing correctly this affects the brain frequencies. This can lead to lack of creativity, poor sleep, anxiety. Studies have show that deep, correct breathing changes the frequencies of the brainwaves to a calmer stage.

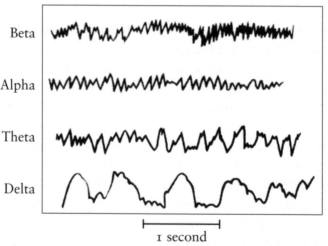

THE FREQUENCIES OF THE BRAIN'S MAGNETIC FIELD
ARE KNOWN AS ALPHA, BETA AND THETA.

THE BRAIN'S TWO MAIN HEMISPHERES ARE KNOWN AS THE LEFT AND THE RIGHT BRAIN

The World Health Organisation has stated that 60% of people in the western world have an over dominant left brain hemisphere.

Creativity is a right brain faculty, other right brain facilities are spirituality, intuition, emotion i.e. love and fear.
Faculties contained within the left brain hemisphere are speech, analytical thinking, mathematical/numbers and scientific thinking.

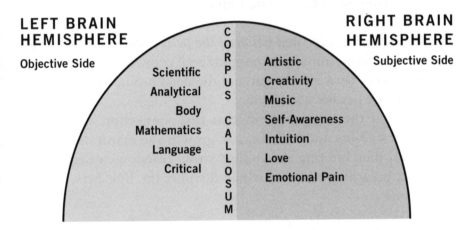

LEFT BRAIN HEMISPHERE
Objective Side

CORPUS CALLOSUM

Scientific
Analytical
Body
Mathematics
Language
Critical

RIGHT BRAIN HEMISPHERE
Subjective Side

Artistic
Creativity
Music
Self-Awareness
Intuition
Love
Emotional Pain

BRAIN RHYTHM FREQUENCIES or 'Gears' are:

BETA	Stress	15-25	cycles per second
ALPHA	Creativity	9-15	cycles per second
THETA	Meditation	5-9	cycles per second
	Trance		
DELTA	Deep Sleep	0-5	cycles per second

General Information about Correct Breathing

Let us consider the excretion or removal of waste material from the body a process which is going on all the time.

Very few people know that it is said that only 3% of this waste material is in solid form i.e. faeces, 7% is eliminated in liquid form as urine and 20% as perspiration.

The remaining 70% is said to be discharged through our exhalation of waste air - amazing isn't it?

To recap:

3% is excreted as solids (faeces)
7% is excreted as liquids (urine)
20% is excreted as perspiration
70% is excreted in the out-breath

Apparently, the brain requires between 30 to 40% of our oxygen intake. It is said we have a second brain which is located in our gut, correct breathing stimulates the second brain.

The second brain is located between the pelvic bone and the navel. Correct Breathing stimulates the emotional connection between the two brains i.e. between the gut and the head brain. Remembering that the heart lies between them.

Amongst the many benefits that this connection activates is emotional stability and balance, true growth and maturation of the individual thus limiting the endless stress reaction caused by the incorrect breathing pattern, which disrupts the link between the two brains.

When our Breathing has been fully perfected our spiritual aspects will be fully functioning. There is a saying that "the higher contains the lower" which means in this instance that when all the other functions are working then the highest function, Spirituality, will be fully functioning. At this stage we will have perfected our breathing.

Correct Breathing stimulates the second brain which is located between the pelvic bone and the naval i.e. the lower belly. This is said to be at the source of the auto immune system, and the brain in this case appears to be the emotional intuitive old wise brain which seems to know the correct answer to otherwise intractable problems

The Abdomen is an organ which is in connection with the upper Brain, generating the vast majority of the body's immune cells and a larger number of neuro transmitters and substances such as seratonin which govern our mental state.

P. Pallardy, Gut Instinct
2nd Edn. London: Rodale International Ltd. (2006), p.128

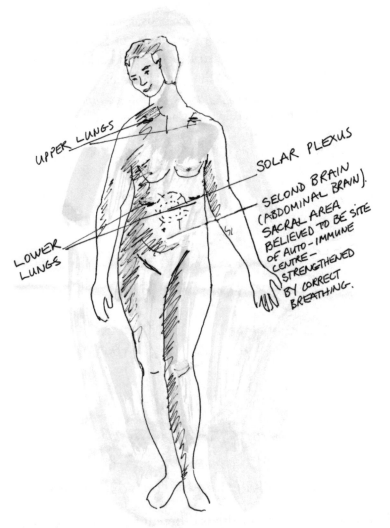

UPPER LUNGS

SOLAR PLEXUS

SECOND BRAIN (ABDOMINAL BRAIN). SACRAL AREA BELIEVED TO BE SITE OF AUTO-IMMUNE CENTRE - STRENGTHENED BY CORRECT BREATHING.

LOWER LUNGS

THE SOLAR PLEXUS, SECOND BRAIN AND SACRAL AREA

Eastern healing traditions have known about the solar plexus for centuries, and seen it as an important part of the nervous system. Western writers have termed the solar plexus the 'abdominal brain' It is composed of white and gray brain matter, similar to that composing the head brain of man.

The name 'solar' is well bestowed on this 'brain' as it radiates strength and energy to all parts of the body, even the upper brain's depending largely upon it as a store-house of Prana. The Solar Plexus is situated in the Epigastric region, just back of the 'pit of the stomach' on either side of the spinal column.

Yogi Ramacharaka, The Science of Breath
London: L. N. Fowler & Co. Ltd. (2005), p.22

BREATH IS KNOWN AS PRANA OR LIFE FORCE IN INDIA

The Eastern model of health is different from our western model and has been used for centuries in India and eastern countries.

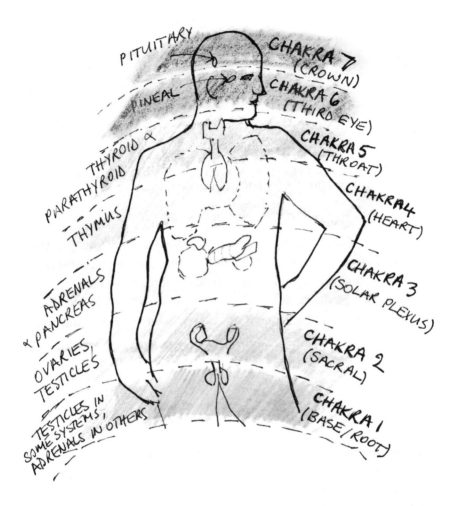

**DIAGRAM SHOWING THE COMMON ASSOCIATIONS BETWEEN
THE CHAKRAS AND THE GLANDS OF THE ENDOCRINE SYSTEM**

Complete breathing leads to the final opening of the crown chakra
Correct Breathing stimulates the main chakras which are known as
base, sacral, solar plexus, heart, throat, brow and crown as they
rise up through the body.

The crown chakra is the last chakra to open as a person reaches
their full spiritual potential.

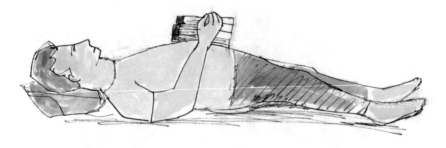

USE OF A LARGE BOOK PLACED ON THE ABDOMEN
TO HELP OPEN UP THE DIAPHRAGM ON THE INHALE

At the beginning of your relaxation practice you will observe that the expanding movement of the abdomen as you breathe starts above the stomach. Correct breathing, when you achieve it will give the sensation that the abdomen is lifted between the pelvic bone and the navel. When the lift starts above the navel it is an indication that the breath has not yet regained its proper function.

Karin Roon, The New Way to Relax
2nd Edn. Glasgow: Phoenix (Scotland) Publishers, (1991)

THE VITAL FORCE

Ancient philosophers often assumed what modern scientists are now beginning to prove that breathing affects our mental and physical wellbeing.

Ancient Greek theories of breathing stem from the work of Plato and Aristotle. Aristotle wrote "The soul is air, air moves and is cognizant. Air that we breathe gives us the soul, life and consciousness." The Pneumatists, inspired by Aristotle's ideas, concluded that air was pneuma - or spirit, the vital force - and was the source of all health and disease.

Our breath connects us to everything that lives, so in breathing correctly we connect deeply with the intricate web of life and nature.

* * *

Questionnaire

GREAT BIG TRUST

PROPOSED MULTIPLE CHOICE QUESTIONS
SCVQ LEVEL 7

Section 1

TICK THE <u>INCORRECT</u> ANSWER FROM a – d

1   The chemical consequences of incorrect breathing are
   a. Disruption of the acid/alkaline balance in the blood
   b. Increased production of adrenalin
   c. The brain gets up to 50% less oxygen than normal
   d. Feeling of calmness

2.   Where are the main sinus areas located?
   a. Above the eyes
   b. Centre of forehead
   c. Side of nose
   d. Back of the neck

3.   Correct breathing
   a. Supplies adequate oxygen to the cells
   b. Warms the air as it enters the nose
   c. Cools the air as it enters the nose
   d. Filters the air before it enters the lungs.

4. Symptoms of health associated with correct breathing
    a. Good circulation
    b. Less requirement for artificial heat
    c. More energy
    d. Difficulty in keeping warm

5. Incorrect breathing can lead to
    a. Tight throat muscles
    b. Feelings of anxiety
    c. Hyperventilation
    d. Increased spirituality

6. What are the faculties contained within the right brain hemisphere?
    a. Emotion
    b. Art
    c. Science
    d. Intuition

7. The site of the apex of the narrow upper lobes of the lungs is situated
    a. At the highest point of the chest.
    b. Below the base of the throat.
    c. Just beneath the collar bone
    d. Just above the diaphragm.

8. The lowest part of the lungs is situated
    a. At the middle of the rib cage
    b. At the base of the back rib cage
    c. Just below the bottom of the front rib cage
    d. At the base of the diaphragm

9. The frequencies of the brain's magnetic field are known as
   a. Alpha
   b. Beta
   c. Theta
   d. Omega

10. Which of the following does not lead directly into the lungs?
    a. Pharynx
    b. Larynx
    c. Ears
    d. Trachea

11. Internal exercise afforded by good diaphragmatic action leads to
    a. Healthy Heart
    b. Clear thinking
    c. Diseased organs
    d. Good skin

12. What are the faculties contained within the left brain hemisphere?
    a. Speech
    b. Analytical thinking
    c. Creative thinking
    d. Mathematical/numbers

Section 2

TICK THE <u>CORRECT</u> ANSWER FROM a – d

1. Where is the location of the diaphragm muscle?
   a. Top of the chest
   b. At base of lower abdomen
   c. Just below the rib cage
   d. Base of spine

2. At what age are we likely to know most about correct breathing?
    a. Fifty seven
    b. Seventeen
    c. Birth
    d. Twenty

3. What are the causes of hyperventilation?
    a. Under breathing
    b. Over breathing
    c. Correct breathing
    d. Breath holding

4. Continuous back pain can be a symptom of correct breathing
    a. Yes
    b. During eating
    c. For a limited period
    d. Never

5. A satisfactory normal breathing pattern to aim for is
    a. 4-6 breaths per minute
    b. 15-22 breaths per minute
    c. 10-14 breaths per minute
    d. 7-9 breaths per minute

6. What percentage of our total oxygen supply is required by the brain?
    a. 10% to 20%
    b. 20% to 30%
    c. 30% to 40%
    d. 40% to 50%

7. What percentage of our waste material is said to be
    eliminated as liquid?
    a. 40%
    b. 8%
    c. 7%
    d. 75%

8. What percentage of our waste material is said to be
    excreted as solids?
    a. 3%
    b. 15%
    c. 25%
    d. 40%

9. What percentage of waste material is apparently eliminated
    through the out-breath?
    a. 17%
    b. 25%
    c. 80%
    d. 70%

10. What percentage of our waste material has been quoted to
    be eliminated through perspiration?
    a. 12%
    b. 30%
    c. 90%
    d. 20%

11. The muscles at the back of the eyes control
    a. 10% of the electrical activity of the brain
    b. 60% of the electrical activity of the brain
    c. 30% of the electrical activity of the brain
    d. 25% of the electrical activity of the brain

12. Correct breathing stimulates the second brain which is located?
    a. At the base of the spine
    b. At the tips of the fingers
    c. Between the pelvic bone and the navel (i.e. lower belly)
    d. At the base of the throat

13. In which part of the world is breath known as prana?
    a. Africa
    b. Brazil
    c. India
    d. Central Europe

14. Only when this area is fully functioning will we have perfected our breathing
    a. Physical
    b. Mental
    c. Spiritual
    d. Emotional

15. Complete breathing leads to the final opening of which chakra?
    a. Base
    b. Throat
    c. Crown chakra
    d. Solar plexus

16. In order to breathe correctly we have first to:
    a. Raise the shoulders
    b. Expand the chest
    c. Expand the lower part of the lungs
    d. Pull in the lower part of the abdomen

17. Good healthy lung tissue will
    a. Resist germs
    b. Encourage germs
    c. Feel hot and cold
    d. Be grey in colour

18. Imperfect breathing allows
    a. a considerable part of the lungs to remain inactive
    b. a considerable part of the lungs to remain active
    c. Healthy cell growth
    d. Improved digestion

19. The quality of blood depends upon
    a. Its proper oxygenation
    b. Wearing warm clothes
    c. Eating black pudding
    d. Living in a hot climate

20. The chest cavity of a correct breather is
    a. Narrow and long
    b. Full and broad
    c. Sagging
    d. Wet and cold

		c.	12.	b.	3.	a.	8.
b.	20.	c.	11.	c.	2	d.	7.
a.	19.	d.	10.	c.	1.	c.	6.
a.	18.	d.	9.	Section Two		d.	5
a.	17.	a.	8.			d.	4.
c.	16.	c.	7.	c.	12.	c.	3.
c.	15.	c.	6.	c.	11.	d.	2
c.	14.	c.	5	c.	10.	d.	1.
c.	13.	d.	4.	d.	9.	Section One	

ANSWERS TO QUESTIONNAIRE

Bibliography

Altman, Nathaniel - *Oxygen Prescription: The Miracle of Oxidative Therapies*. Healing Arts Press, 2007

Bach, Edward - *Heal Thyself: Explanation of the Real Cause and Cure of Disease*. C. W. Daniel, 1996

Beeken, Jenny, and Stenhouse, Janita - *Don't Hold Your Breath: Breathing for Vitality, Yogic Breathing and More....: A Guide to Good Breathing*. Polair Publishing, 2004

Bradley, Dinah, and Thomas, Mike, Dr. - *Hyperventilation Syndrome: Breathing Pattern Disorders and How to Overcome Them*. Kyle Books, 2011

Capra, Fritjof - *The Tao of Physics*. Flamingo, 1992

Clifton-Smith, Tania, and Collins, Sandy - *Breathe to Succeed in All Aspects of Your Life*. Penguin Books, 1999

Daemion, Jonathon - *The Healing Power of Breath: An Introduction to Holistic Breath Therapy*. Prism Press, 1989

Dumont, Theron Q. - *The Solar Plexus or Abdominal Brain*. Cosimo Inc., 2007

Feild, Reshad, *Breathing Alive: A Guide to Conscious Living*. AuthorHouse, 2008

Hay, Louise L. - *You Can Heal Your Life*, HayHouse, 2004

Here's Health magazine, August 1983. *Body and Soul. Life in the Slow Lane.*

Hotema, Hilton - *Man's Higher Consciousness (1962)*. Kessinger Publishing, 2010

Kent, Howard - *Breathe Better, Feel Better*. Greenwich, 2001

Knowles, William P. - *New Life Through Breathing*. Allen & Unwin, 1966

Ley, R., and Timmons, B. H. - *Behavioral and Psychological Approaches to Breathing Disorders*. Springer, 1994

Manne, Joy - *Conscious Breathing - How Shamanic Breathwork Can Transform Your Life*. North Atlantic Books, US. Sept 2004

Minett, Gunnel - *Exhale: An Overview of Breathwork*. Floris Books, 2004

Morningstar, Jim, *Breathing in Light and Love: Your Call to Breath and Body Mastery*. Transformation Inc., 1994

Orr, Leonard D. - *Breath Awareness:Breath Awareness for Public Schools, Medical Profession*. Inspiration Univiverdsity, 1988

Pallardy, Pierre - *Gut Instinct: What Your Stomach is Trying to Tell You: 7 Easy Steps to Health and Healing*. Rodale, 2007

Ramacharaka, Yogi - *The Hindu-Yogi Science of Breath*. BiblioBazaar, 2007

Roon, Karin - *The New Way To Relax*. Phoenix Publishers, 1991

Scovel Shinn, Florence - *Writings of Florence Scovel Shinn*. DeVorss & Company, 1999

Shearer, Anne Gillard, - *Love, Drugs or Any City Like Glasgow: The Source of the Addicted Society*. A. G. Shearer, 1987

Swatmarama, Swami - *Hatha Yoga Pradipika*. Forgotten Books, 2008

Tolle, Eckhart - *A New Earth: Create a Better Life*. Penguin Books, 2009

de Vries, Jan - *Air: The Breath of Life*. Mainstream Publishing, 1994

* * *